COLLECTOR'S
VALUE

Charming Tails®

Secondary Market Price Guide
& Collector Handbook
SECOND EDITION

Managing Editor:	Jeff Mahony	Creative Director:	Joe T. Nguyen
Associate Editors:	Melissa A. Bennett	Production Supervisor:	Scott Sierakowski
	Jan Cronan	Assistant Art Director:	Lance Doyle
	Gia C. Manalio	Senior Graphic Designers:	Susannah C. Judd
	Paula Stuckart		David S. Maloney
Contributing Editor:	Mike Micciulla		Carole Mattia-Slater
Editorial Assistants:	Timothy R. Affleck	Graphic Designers:	Jennifer J. Bennett
	Heather N. Carreiro		Sean-Ryan Dudley
	Jennifer Filipek		Kimberly Eastman
	Beth Hackett		Marla B. Gladstone
	Nicole LeGard Lenderking		Robert Kyerematen
	Steven Shinkaruk		Angi Shearstone
	Joan C. Wheal		David Ten Eyck
Web Reporter:	Samantha Bouffard	Art Interns:	Huy Hoang
Editorial Intern:	Dan Ten Eyck		Anna Zagajewska
		Web Graphic Designer:	Ryan Falis
		Product Development Manager:	Paul Rasid
		R&D Specialist:	Priscilla Berthiaume

ISBN 1-58598-052-8

CheckerBee
PUBLISHING

306 Industrial Park Road • Middletown, CT 06457

www.collectorbee.com

Table Of Contents

Introducing The Collector's Value Guide™

*W*elcome to the second edition of the Collector's Value Guide™ to Charming Tails®. Since their introduction as a small group of ornaments in 1992, the line has attracted an enthusiastic following of collectors charmed by the adventures of Mackenzie and Maxine Mouse and their animal friends. Whether this is your first trip to Squashville or you are a frequent visitor, this guide will help you get the most out of your collection.

Our full-color Value Guide is indispensable for staying up-to-date on the new releases and retirements for the figurines, ornaments and other related products that comprise the Charming Tails collection. It also provides stock numbers, original prices and newly updated market values that reflect secondary market prices from across the country.

So sit back, relax and get ready to be transported to a magical land where mice type away on apple computers, raccoons travel in pumpkin cars and skunks deliver the mail. Once you "leaf" through the Collector's Value Guide™, you'll never look at wildlife the same way again!

Look Inside To Find:

- An interview with Charming Tails artist Dean Griff
- The latest news and information on *The Leaf & Acorn Club*®
- Display tips for showcasing your collection
- The top five most valuable Charming Tails pieces
- An in-depth look at the members of the Charming Tails family
- And much, much more!

Charming Tails® Overview

*W*hile wild mice, squirrels and raccoons can sometimes be a nuisance, the animals in Dean Griff's Charming Tails collection are the exact opposite. These friendly critters are as lovable as can be, and they're just as willing to give affection as they are to get it.

GETTING STARTED

Griff's charming characters have been making their way into the hearts of collectors across America since 1992, when the Silvestri Corporation, a subsidiary of Fitz and Floyd®, introduced the woodland creatures in eight Christmas ornaments. The line expanded to include baskets, candleholders and other giftware items, but was not considered to be a collectible until 1994, when it introduced its first dated ornament, "A Mackenzie Snowball." The change from a giftware line to a collectible line came quickly, as the first numbered pieces were added to the line in 1995, and two limited editions, "Mackenzie Building A Snowman" and "Sleigh Ride" made their way into the collection in 1996. This was soon followed by more limited editions, exclusives, special event pieces and early releases, all of which helped to propel Charming Tails to collectible status.

THE ROAD TO SUCCESS

The collection, which was called The Woodland Collection in 1993 before changing its name to Charming Tails in 1994, has continued to grow in popularity. In fact, the collection was so popular that even when Fitz and Floyd sold Silvestri in 1996, it retained the Charming Tails line.

Two major events occured in the next two years which would establish Charming Tails' position as a leader in the collectibles industry. In 1997, *The Leaf & Acorn Club*, the line's official collectors' club, debuted. The club was the natural extension of The Acorn Society, which had been launched in 1996 at the Rosemont Collectible Exposition and served as the foundation for the expanded *The Leaf & Acorn Club*. The club is still running strong today, as it enters its third year of existence. One year after the debut of the club, in 1998, artist Dean Griff was honored with the "Artist of the Year" award from the National Association of Limited Edition Dealers (NALED), one of the most prestigious awards in the industry.

Since then, the Charming Tails collection has garnered numerous other awards, as well as a strong and steady fan base. In addition to *The Leaf & Acorn Club*, there are several local clubs which have formed across the nation to unite collectors with other Charming Tails fans in their area. Several on-line clubs have also been established. Ask your local retailer if there is a local Charming Tails club chapter near you, or log onto the Internet and search for "Charming Tails clubs" for more information about on-line clubs.

A FAMILY AFFAIR

What makes the Charming Tails collection so successful? While they might be cute animals to some, the characters in the Charming Tails collection take on human actions and emotions that allow us to relate to their situations. Each character has a different personality, expressed through its antics and expressions, which makes it special and brings it to life.

Much of the line's appeal is in the sense of family and community that is found within each piece. Based in the tiny animal town of Squashville, the figurines depict the ups and downs of everyday life through the 11 main characters. Couples Mackenzie & Maxine Mouse and Binkey & Bunnie Bunny lead the pack, as they are the most recognizable of the characters, and they make up the majority of the figurines. Over the years, however, they have been joined by many friends and neighbors, including Stewart Skunk, Chauncey

Chipmunk, Reginald Raccoon, Lydia Ladybug, Sidney Snail, Sebastian & Sabrina Squirrel. (For more information on the Charming Tails characters, see *A Very Charming Family* on page 10). Anyone who is part of a family or close-knit community will find it easy to identify with these comical critters and collectors soon find that they feel like a part of the Squashville family themselves.

WINTER, SPRING, SUMMER AND FALL

Back when it was solely a giftware line, Charming Tails pieces were designed primarily with seasonal themes, specifically autumn and Christmas. These themes still exist today, and you can find your favorite Charming Tails characters enjoying "Easter" (which also incorporates general spring themes), "Halloween," "Autumn Harvest" and the "Lazy Days" of summer. The "Deck The Halls" series of ornaments is also available to capture the spirit of Christmas, and "Squashville" features residents of the town participating in a plethora of winter activities such as caroling, sledding, snowshoeing and even building snowbunnies and snowmice!

In addition to the seasonal themes and the general "Charming Tails" pieces, many other specific catagories have been created. "The Wedding" features the union of Mackenzie and Maxine Mouse, as they proclaim their love for one another in front of a few close

DEAN GRIFF – TELEVISION CELEBRITY!

Can't get enough of Charming Tails? You can now find Mackenzie, Maxine and all of their friends on television! Dean Griff makes several television appearances per year on the television home shopping network, QVC. During his shows, many exclusive Charming Tails pieces have been available and retirement announcements are also not uncommon! Check your television listings or the QVC web site for a detailed list of upcoming shows.

friends. "Love Is In The Air" features a series of pieces perfect for Valentine's Day, as the critters cuddle up to the ones they love and celebrate the true meaning of romance.

A SMALL WORLD

In 1998, Griff expanded his Charming Tails portfolio with a line of miniature pieces called Teeny Tiny Tails™. Perfect for smaller collectors (or those with less shelf space), Teeny Tiny Tails were miniature versions of the Squashville residents. Nine pieces were released in the collection, all based around the theme, "The Squashville County Fair." Included in this nostalgic scene were three musical rides, an authentic ticket booth, a candy apple booth and games that offered large prizes, as a baby mouse discovered in "The Big Winner." The Teeny Tiny Tails collection retired in 1999.

BACK TO BASICS

Through the years, artist Dean Griff has released a number of Charming Tails accessories, including candleholders, musicals and waterglobes, among other items. Recently, Griff has turned his attention to designing a line of giftware featuring his Charming Tails characters designed to perfectly complement any room in the home.

No matter what the occasion, the Charming Tails collection has a piece which is right for everyone. And with such a variety of characters, the residents of Squashville are sure to keep entertaining collectors with their delightful antics for years to come.

A Very Charming Family

*L*ong ago, a shooting star fell from the sky, passing over a forest on its way to the ground. Magic dust from the star settled on the forest floor, bringing the land to life. Soon forest greenery such as acorns and pumpkins were transformed into beautiful buildings and vehicles. And no sooner had the forest flora taken on a life of its own, a group of friends stumbled upon the newly-formed town. They made this enchanted place their home, and named it Squashville. Since then, several new friends have settled into Squashville, each bringing their own charming characteristics to the close-knit community.

MACKENZIE & MAXINE MOUSE

Mackenzie & Maxine Mouse, Squashville's "First Couple," serve as leaders within the community. The fun-loving duo, who tied the knot in 1998, are known throughout town for their sense of adventure and their ability to have a good time no matter what. Charming Tails artist Dean Griff has mentioned in previous interviews that Mackenzie displays the characteristics that he would most like to have.

BINKIE & BUNNIE BUNNY

Binkie & Bunnie Bunny are Squashville's number one sweethearts. They enjoy "An Abundance Of Love" for one another, and can usually be caught doing a little snuggling or smooching, especially during spring, their favorite season. Because of their gentle nature, the Bunnys are loved by everyone in town. This couple, as well as Mackenzie & Maxine Mouse, serve as the heart of the Charming Tails family.

CHAUNCEY CHIPMUNK

Chauncey may be a little shy at first, but once you get to know him, you can't imagine life without him. Loyal through thick and thin, Chauncey loves spending time "Toasting Marshmallows" with friends and enjoying the great outdoors. Dean Griff has mentioned that Chauncey is based on his own personality and character traits.

STEWART SKUNK

Known as the carefree spirit of the group, Stewart insists on having fun in all that he does! From lounging in the sun to acting as the "Little Drummer Boy," Stewart is sure to give it his all! His favorite activities include basking in the sun on warm, summer days and celebrating the spirit of Christmas with his friends and neighbors in Squashville.

REGINALD RACCOON

Reginald, Squashville's own practical joker, loves to have fun! He feels that a smile is one's most beautiful feature, and can usually be found sporting his own devilish grin! From helping Mackenzie to earn his "Training Wings" to leading the town parade as "The Drum Major," times spent with Reginald are anything but boring!

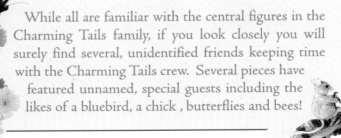

ALL IN THE FAMILY

While all are familiar with the central figures in the Charming Tails family, if you look closely you will surely find several, unidentified friends keeping time with the Charming Tails crew. Several pieces have featured unnamed, special guests including the likes of a bluebird, a chick, butterflies and bees!

LYDIA LADYBUG

Lydia can always brighten up the day with her brilliant red color and positive attitude. Her friends know that they can count on her to be around whether they are happy or feeling blue. She loves to travel, and can almost always be found "Along For The Ride" with her friends who are on the go.

SIDNEY SNAIL

Sidney serves as a silent companion to his friends in Squashville. Always there to lend a helping hand, he has become a natural fixture in Squashville society. Sidney moved into the Squashville neighborhood soon after his good friend Lydia Ladybug, and instantly fell in love with his new friends and neighbors!

SEBASTIAN AND SABRINA SQUIRREL

Naturally nervous Sebastian usually finds it hard to make friends. But he couldn't resist the warmth of the residents of Squashville, and now finds himself a regular part of the community, participating in everything from joining the "Charming Choo Choo" to playing "Ring Around The Rosie." Sabrina is just as "nuts" over Squashville as she is over her main squeeze Sebastian, whom she taught that "You Can't Run From Love." Young and full of life, Sabrina is eager to participate in all of the Squashville fun, and looks forward to a long future with her newfound friends.

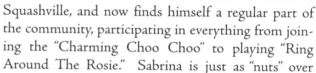

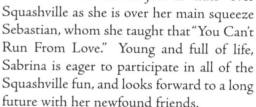

Dean Griff Biography

*I*t was during his childhood in rustic Oneida, New York, that Dean Griff was introduced to the woodland creatures who would later become the inspiration for his Charming Tails figurines. Growing up, Griff and his siblings were responsible for helping tend to the animals on the family farm. When his chores were complete, Griff spent hours walking through the nearby woods and watching the forest creatures build their homes. He also developed a love for art during this time, and spent many hours drawing and painting murals on the walls of the family barn. As he grew older, Griff studied art at Stockbridge Valley Central School. His parents encouraged his interest, and Griff credits them as his inspiration for pursuing a career in art rather than in the agricultural world in which he was raised.

At the age of 23, Griff accepted a job as an assistant to the Curator of the Syracuse University Art Collection. In his spare time, he continued to draw and paint, and won several awards in university art shows. In addition, Griff began designing hand-painted ornaments, which he gave to his friends for the holidays.

In 1989, Dean accepted a job in Florida as a set decorator for television programs and commercials. One year later, he met with the Director of Product Development for a major giftware manufacturer. Griff agreed to create a small line of Christmas ornaments for the company. The ornaments were introduced to the market as The Woodland Collection, which later became known as Charming Tails.

Although Griff has moved a long way from his family's farm in Oneida, he still cherishes the memories of his childhood there. The values of his family, especially his mother's sense of humor, coupled with the childlike mischief he and his siblings created on the farm, have had a major role in the wonderful Charming Tails pieces he creates today.

Q&A With Dean Griff

*C*heckerBee Publishing once again had the opportunity to speak with award-winning Charming Tails designer Dean Griff about his wonderful woodland creations.

CheckerBee: Growing up on a farm, did you envision scenes similar to those experienced by your Charming Tails characters?

Dean Griff: As a child on the farm, I watched the animals in their everyday lives and could see the personalities of some of my own family members in them. In my imagination, the animals would think and feel the same as anyone of us. I envisioned them making tidy little homes hidden away in the woods with all the same comforts I enjoyed living in my parents' home. Even though I left childhood many, many years ago, I still like to believe that animals can feel love and happiness just like we do.

CheckerBee: Can you tell us how you got your start in the collectibles industry?

Dean Griff: I found my way into the world of collectibles through nothing more than luck. Back in 1991, I attended a party for a friend and brought them a glass Christmas ornament I had painted a wildlife scene on. Unknown to me, another guest at the party, Marje Reed, who was the head of product development for a Christmas ornament company, was shown the ornament I had painted. Marje then asked me if I would be interested in sending her some designs for possible development. After explaining to her that I had never really designed anything before and didn't know what to do, she convinced me to send her a dozen drawings "just to see."

FAMILY TIES

Artist Dean Griff has said in the past that much of his inspiration comes from his childhood and the time spent with his family. With three brothers and two sisters, that's a lot of memories to help him with his work!

A few weeks later, as I sat at my desk to begin the first of the dozen designs, I didn't know what to draw. With the blank white paper staring back at me, I drew a pair of eyes onto the page and shaded them in. I usually begin drawing with the eyes because many years ago, my grandfather told me that the eyes are the windows to the soul and if you get the eyes right the rest just falls into place. As I looked at the eyes on the paper, they appeared to me to be the eyes of a mouse, so I drew a mouse around them and Mackenzie was born.

After completing eleven more drawings and painting them in, I sent them off to Marje. One year later, these twelve drawings had been transformed into ornaments and were being sold across the country. As they say, the rest is history.

CheckerBee: How have your past career experiences influenced your art?

Dean Griff: The biggest influence on my artwork from my past work experiences comes from the job I have held the longest. Being a

farmhand on my parents' farm not only taught me the value of loving nature but of how important it is to truly enjoy your work. I really owe a mountain of gratitude to my parents for instilling in me from a very early age a strong work ethic. They were also influential in giving me the ability to find immense pleasure in the world around me.

CheckerBee: What do you think you would be doing today if you had never pursued your interest in art?

Dean Griff: I think that I would still be working in the film industry doing set decorating and designing. This is what I was doing until just a couple of years ago when my travel schedule for Charming Tails signings made it impossible to take on any more television production projects. I have always found enjoyment from working no matter what the job. Of course, my present job designing Charming Tails does have a wonderful bonus of meeting so many nice people.

CheckerBee: What was the first Charming Tails piece that you created and what memories do you carry from the experience?

Dean Griff: The very first Charming Tails piece I designed was "The Drifters." This is a piece that has a tiny mouse holding onto an autumn leaf using it as a parachute. It was November of 1991 and I had been living in Florida for about two years. I was feeling very homesick for the beautiful autumns back on the farm in New York so I drew an orange leaf for the little mouse to hold onto. The reason I drew a mouse is, as I explained earlier, it was all in the eyes. After drawing those eyes on the paper they just looked like a mouse's eyes, so a mouse it was.

CheckerBee: Do you see yourself in any specific character or does a little bit of you appear in each?

Dean Griff: There is a little bit of me in each of the Charming Tails characters or at least each character has personality traits I wish I had. Mackenzie, who is very outgoing, is the character I wish I could be like. Chauncey, who is very shy and tends to step to the side of the limelight, is the character I am. Through the characters of Charming Tails, I have found an outlet for the mischief and humor that lay just under the surface of my own shyness.

CheckerBee: Can you tell us a little bit about where some of your inspiration for new pieces comes from?

Dean Griff: Most of my inspiration comes from my memories of growing up on the farm and from the wonderful humor possessed by my family members. I have written down page after page of ideas yet to be drawn out based on my memories of family life. It has been very rewarding for me as I travel around the country and meet so many people who share the same kind of family experiences.

CheckerBee: Do you ever get "artist's block?" If so, how do you conquer it?

Dean Griff: I have been very lucky in regards to "artist's block." I encounter minor bouts of it from time to time, usually after taking a few days off from daily drawing. The process I go through to conquer the block takes about a day. If I can, a walk in the woods is a sure-fire way to conquer the block, but many times the opportunity for a wooded walk doesn't exist. In those cases, I review a notebook of ideas that I keep and start making quick thumbnail sketches from them. In a short time, I find my mind wandering off to dozens of other ideas that aren't written in the notebook and I no longer am "blocked." Of course, the down side to this is that I then get a flood of ideas and have a hard time selecting which one I should do first.

CheckerBee: Your appearances at collectibles shows always draw quite a crowd. How does it feel to be in the spotlight?

Dean Griff: The "spotlight" really has never been important to me and honestly is something I used to try to avoid. Whenever I find

myself in that situation, it's like I'm standing back watching someone else. After an event, when I return home, it feels like a dream, something distant and unreal that happened to someone other than me. I design Charming Tails because I love to design and meeting so many wonderful collectors, whom I like to think of as my friends, is a real bonus. As for the "spotlight," we can save that for Maxine and Mackenzie.

MORE GRIFF GIFTS

Before signing an exclusive contract with Fitz and Floyd, Griff designed many pieces for companies such as Christopher Radko, Roman Giftware and Silvestri. These items, which include snowmen, bears and more, came as figurines and giftware.

CheckerBee: Are there any upcoming story lines we can look forward to?

Dean Griff: The story and family of Charming Tails is ever growing. There are a few surprises planned for the future and maybe a new friend or two, but to keep all the fun going, I really can't say too much more right now. Just keep watching!

CheckerBee: In 1998, you were named NALED's "Artist Of The Year." How do you feel about that status?

Dean Griff: It was an honor to be named "Artist Of The Year" and a huge surprise! I'm a huge fan of Thomas Blackshear, who I feel is a wonderful artist, and I was so sure that he was going to be named "Artist Of The Year" that when they announced that I won I felt there must have been a mistake. I am happy to say that in 1999 Thomas did win the honor of "Artist Of The Year" and I am humbled to be put in such good company.

CheckerBee: You have been extremely active in dedicating proceeds from your pieces to various charities. How do you decide which charities to contribute to?

Dean Griff: The two charities I have donated to thus far were selected based on experiences with close friends. The first charity was AmFar, selected in memory of the friends I have lost to AIDS. The newest charity, The Candlelighters Childhood Cancer Foundation, was selected on behalf of so many collectors and personal friends who are dealing with or have lost someone to cancer.

CheckerBee: What would you like to tell your fans?

Dean Griff: I would just like to say thank you for allowing me to be a part of your lives. The friendship extended to the Charming Tails family and to me is a priceless gift that I am greatly honored by. Your friendship is the brightest star I could ever hope to reach!

What's New For Charming Tails®

*T*his section highlights the new Charming Tails pieces introduced for 2000. To date, 30 new figurines and six ornaments have been released.

CHARMING TAILS®

Apple Of My Eye (LE-2000). . . It should be clear to everyone who the apple of Mackenzie's eye is – why it's Maxine of course! Surrounded by fragrant apple blossoms, Maxine is sure to catch your eye too.

A Bubbly Personality . . . Mackenzie's fun-loving spirit gets him into a bit of "bubble trouble," and he has to be careful not to get "carried away" by all the soapy bubbles he has blown. Even Lydia can't help but join in on the fun!

Congraduations . . . Mackenzie knows the importance of education and he shows his enthusiasm by giving a "hats off" in this new figurine. This salute to schooling makes a perfect gift for any recent graduate!

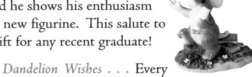

Dandelion Wishes . . . Every mouse knows that dandelions have the magical power to grant wishes. So who can blame Mackenzie for trying his luck with one on such a warm, sunny day? But don't ask what he's wishing for because if he tells it won't come true!

Morning Hare . . . Even an early bird like Bunnie finds the need to jump-start her day with a cup of coffee while perusing the morning paper. And if you've ever wondered what bunnies wear on their feet, now you know – bunny slippers!

Wash Away Those Worries . . . Mom always knows how to wash away the memory of the latest scraped knee or tumble off a bike. So it's no wonder that Bunnie's little one doesn't mind a quick scrub in the tub. Feeling clean makes the whole day brighter!

EASTER

Chickie Chariot Ride . . . Mackenzie sure knows how to get around in style as he hitches a ride from this cute baby chick. A trip through the countryside to visit some good friends is always a great way to spend a spring day.

Ducky Weather . . . Mackenzie and Sidney might be taking cover, but for a duck there's nothing better than a spring shower. With any luck, there will be plenty of puddles for this duck to splash around in and plenty of sunshine for everyone else.

LOVE IS IN THE AIR

An Abundance Of Love . . . Binkey and Bunnie always have plenty of love to go around. Which is a good thing for this large family! The saying "the more the merrier" has never been truer than in this happy group.

Candy Kisses . . . What could be sweeter than a kiss from your sweetie? Nothing, but a little chocolate sure doesn't hurt! As they dip into their Valentine's Day treats, these two sweethearts can't resist stealing a chocolate-covered kiss.

Give Love A Shot . . . Mackenzie wants everyone to have the special kind of love he and Maxine share. So with the aid of his trusty slingshot, he's out to do some matchmaking. And you will be hard-pressed to resist his endearing message!

Love Birds . . . These two birds don't seem to need any help from Mackenzie, a.k.a. Cupid. But maybe they did need a little nudge in the right direction. Mackenzie is there just to ensure that everything goes according to plan.

We're A Perfect Fit . . . Mackenzie and Maxine couldn't get any closer than in this sweater built for two. Maxine spent all day knitting this extra large outfit and it certainly looks warm and cozy. They might have a little trouble getting around in it, though!

LAZY DAYS

Adventure Bound . . . Binkey and Mackenzie have set sail for a day of adventure. What more could you possibly need besides a loyal friend, a sturdy raft and a fishing pole? Well, maybe a compass and some wind would help.

Beach Bunnie . . . Bunnie is all set for a day of fun in the sun, surf and sand. Armed with a beach ball, a pail and a shovel, she has everything she needs to keep herself entertained. The only thing Bunnie's missing is someone to share the fun with!

Catching Fireflies . . . On a warm summer night, Maxine always enjoys the challenge of catching fireflies. It takes a trained eye and a skilled hand but Maxine finally snares one of the elusive critters.

Hang Ten . . . Mackenzie "catches the wave" of a popular summer pastime – surfing! He's the Big Kahuna of Squashville as he rides a wave back to shore.

A Real Lifesaver . . . There's nothing to fear with this lifeguard on duty. And because the Squashville residents are such firm practitioners of the buddy system, there won't be too many emergencies for fearless Mackenzie to handle.

Autumn Breezes . . . Fall is in the air and so is Mackenzie! At least, he will be if he lets go of that pumpkin. Although the crisp autumn air signals an end to the summertime fun, there will be plenty of frolicking to be had in the fall leaves.

Be Thankful For Friends . . . Autumn is a time of plenty for these woodland creatures. And who better to share the bounty with than a group of friends? The residents of Squashville take time out to say "thanks" for their caring neighbors.

Put On A Happy Face . . . With two masks to choose from, Mackenzie is more than ready for Halloween. But he clearly prefers the happy-faced mask – who wouldn't? And it's obvious that Sidney whole-heartedly agrees with his decision.

What A Hoot! . . . "Who" could be better at telling jokes than an owl? This one always has his joke book handy and never forgets the punchline. Certainly no one's better at listening to jokes than Mackenzie – he just loves to laugh!

SQUASHVILLE

Dive Into The Holidays . . . Who wants a little mouse with their eggnog? Mackenzie and Maxine get a head-start on the holidays with a quick dip in the eggnog. This traditional Squashville recipe is sure to lift anyone's spirits.

Just The Right Size . . . This little bunny just couldn't wait to build a snowman with Mom. They built their snowmen to scale and no detail was left unattended – Mom's even has a matching holly sprig!

Charming Tails® Top Five

 his section showcases the five most valuable pieces in the Charming Tails collection based on their current secondary market values.

Mouse On Vine Candleholder
Candleholder, #87/504
Issued 1994 – Retired 1995
Issue Price: $55
Secondary Market Price: $500

Pyramid With Mice Candleholder
Candleholder, #87/509
Issued 1994 – Retired 1995
Issue Price: $40
Secondary Market Price: $475

Mouse On Vine Wreath
Wreath, #87/505
Issued 1994 – Retired 1995
Issue Price: $55
Secondary Market Price: $430

Mice On Vine Basket
Basket, #87/506
Issued 1994 – Retired 1995
Issue Price: $55
Secondary Market Price: $425

Mouse On Dragonfly
Ornament, #89/320
Issued 1994 – Retired 1994
Issue Price: $16.50
Secondary Market Price: $415

HOW TO USE YOUR VALUE GUIDE

After Lunch Snooze
Issued: 1995 • Retired: 1997
Original Price: $15
Market Value: $33

#89/558

2

1. LOCATE your piece in the Value Guide. Figurines are listed first, followed by ornaments. Miscellaneous Charming Tails collectibles (baskets, candleholders, votives, musicals, etc.) come next, then club pieces. In the figurine and ornament sections, pieces are listed alphabetically within their designated categories, which are presented (where applicable) in the following order: "Charming Tails," "Easter," "Love Is In The Air," "The Wedding," "Lazy Days," "Halloween/Autumn Harvest," "Squashville" and "Deck The Halls." Each category is followed by an alphabetical listing of any sub-categories that apply. Handy alphabetical and numerical indexes can be found in the back of the book. Note: some items pictured are prototypes and may differ slightly from the actual piece.

Charming Tails

	Price Paid	Value
1.	$15	$33
2.		
3.		
4.		
5.		
6.		
Totals	$15	$33

2. FIND the market value of your piece. Pieces for which secondary market pricing is not established are listed as "N/E." The market value for current pieces is the 2000 suggested retail price.

3. RECORD the original price that you paid and the market value in the corresponding boxes at the bottom of the page.

4. CALCULATE the value for the page by adding all of the boxes in each column. Use a pencil so you can change the totals as your collection grows!

5. TRANSFER the totals from each page to the "Total Value Of My Collection" worksheet on page 98.

6. ADD all of the totals together to determine the overall value of your collection.

> In the Value Guide, the issue year refers to the year the piece became available in stores, although pieces are sometimes announced the previous year.

CHARMING TAILS® FIGURINES

Mackenzie, Maxine, Binkey, Bunnie and all their friends are back in 30 new figurines introduced for the year 2000. To date, the total number of pieces in the figurine collection has risen to over 300, several of which have already been retired. The pieces are divided into several sections, the newest of which is 1999's "Love Is In The Air," a tribute to romance.

1   #85/403

Acorn Built For Two
Issued: 1993 • Current
Original Price: $10
Market Value: $12.50

---

2   #89/558

After Lunch Snooze
Issued: 1995 • Retired: 1997
Original Price: $15
Market Value: $33

3   #89/624

**Ahhh-Chooo!
Get Well Soon**
Issued: 1997 • Current
Original Price: $12
Market Value: $14

4   #89/100

Along For The Ride
Issued: 1999 • Current
Original Price: $18.50
Market Value: $18.50

---

5   #89/110

New!

**Apple Of My Eye
(LE-2000)**
Issued: 2000 • Current
Original Price: $19
Market Value: $19

6   #87/391

The Berry Best
Issued: 1996 • Current
Original Price: $16
Market Value: $17.50

CHARMING TAILS		
	Price Paid	Value
1.		
2.		
3.		
4.		
5.		
6.		
Totals		

Figurines

1   #89/605

Binkey Growing Carrots
Issued: 1995 • Retired: 1995
Original Price: $15
Market Value: $65

2   #89/305

Binkey In A Lily
Issued: 1994 • Retired: 1996
Original Price: $16
Market Value: $55

3   #98/349

Binkey's First Cake
Issued: 1995 • Retired: 1997
Original Price: $16
Market Value: $42

4   #89/586

Binkey's New Pal
Issued: 1995 • Retired: 1996
Original Price: $14
Market Value: $38

5   #89/109

New!

A Bubbly Personality
Issued: 2000 • Current
Original Price: $17
Market Value: $17

6   #89/619

Bunny Buddies
Issued: 1997 • Current
Original Price: $20
Market Value: $22

7   #89/606

Butterfly Smelling Zinnias
Issued: 1995 • Retired: 1995
Original Price: $15
Market Value: $80

8   #89/600

Can I Keep Him?
(LE-2,500)
Issued: 1994 • Sold Out: 1995
Original Price: $13
Market Value: $400

CHARMING TAILS

	Price Paid	Value
1.		
2.		
3.		
4.		
5.		
6.		
7.		
8.		
Totals		

Value Guide — CHARMING TAILS®

1 #87/423

Catchin' Butterflies
Issued: 1996 • Retired: 1998
Original Price: $16
Market Value: $30

2 #87/448

Cattail Catapult
Issued: 1996 • Retired: 1998
Original Price: $16
Market Value: $30

3 #87/690

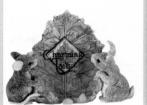

**Charming Tails
Display Sign**
Issued: 1996 • Current
Original Price: $20
Market Value: $22

4 #87/386

The Chase Is On
Issued: 1996 • Retired: 1998
Original Price: $16
Market Value: $34

5 #89/607

**Chauncey Growing
Tomatoes**
Issued: 1995 • Retired: 1995
Original Price: $15
Market Value: $63

6 #98/206

**A Collection Of Friends
(International Collectible
Exposition Piece,
LE-7,500)**
Issued: 1998 • Sold Out: 1998
Original Price: $22
Market Value: $60

7 #89/106

New!

Congraduations
Issued: 2000 • Current
Original Price: $17
Market Value: $17

8 #89/107

New!

Dandelion Wishes
Issued: 2000 • Current
Original Price: $18
Market Value: $18

CHARMING TAILS		
	Price Paid	Value
1.		
2.		
3.		
4.		
5.		
6.		
7.		
8.		
Totals		

1   #89/705

Even The Ups And Downs Are Fun
Issued: 1998 • Retired: 2000
Original Price: $16.50
Market Value: $25

2   #98/417

Feeding Time (GCC Early Release)
Issued: 1995 • Retired: 1996
Original Price: $16
Market Value: $68

3   #89/608

Flower Friends
Issued: 1997 • Retired: 1998
Original Price: $15
Market Value: $30

4   #89/601

Fragile – Handle With Care (LE-15,000)
Issued: 1997 • Sold Out: 1997
Original Price: $18
Market Value: $50
("Love Doesn't Come With Instructions" – $130)

5   #98/213

Friendship In Bloom (NALED/Parkwest Exclusive)
Issued: 1999 • Retired: 1999
Original Price: $17
Market Value: $35

6   #87/364

Gardening Break
Issued: 1996 • Current
Original Price: $16
Market Value: $18

CHARMING TAILS

	Price Paid	Value
1.		
2.		
3.		
4.		
5.		
6.		
7.		
8.		
Totals		

7   #89/102

A Gift Of Love
Issued: 1999 • Current
Original Price: $18
Market Value: $18

8   #97/719

Get Well Soon
Issued: 1994 • Retired: 1997
Original Price: $15
Market Value: $45

Value Guide — Charming Tails®

1	#97/716

Good Luck
Issued: 1994 • Current
Original Price: $15
Market Value: $17.50

2	#89/714

Guess What!
Issued: 1997 • Retired: 1999
Original Price: $16.50
Market Value: $28

3	#98/600

Hang On!
(GCC Exclusive)
Issued: 1997 • Retired: 1998
Original Price: $18
Market Value: $36

4	#89/623

Hangin' Around
Issued: 1997 • Current
Original Price: $18
Market Value: $20

5	#97/715

Happy Birthday
Issued: 1994 • Current
Original Price: $15
Market Value: $17.50

6	#89/717

Hear, Speak &
See No Evil
Issued: 1998 • Current
Original Price: $17.50
Market Value: $18.50

7	#89/760

Hi Cookie
Issued: 1999 • Current
Original Price: $17.50
Market Value: $17.50

8	#89/307

Hide & Seek Mice
Issued: 1994 • Retired: 1994
Original Price: $13.50
Market Value: $350

CHARMING TAILS

	Price Paid	Value
1.		
2.		
3.		
4.		
5.		
6.		
7.		
8.		

Totals

33

1 #89/763

The Honeymoon's Over
Issued: 1999 • Current
Original Price: $20
Market Value: $20

2 #97/723

Hope You're Feeling Better
Issued: 1994 • Retired: 1997
Original Price: $15
Market Value: $40

3 #87/425

Hoppity Hop
Issued: 1996 • Retired: 1998
Original Price: $14
Market Value: $35

4 #98/461

How Do You Measure Love?
Issued: 1994 • Retired: 1996
Original Price: $15
Market Value: $56

5 #89/713

How Many Candles?
Issued: 1998 • Current
Original Price: $16.50
Market Value: $17.50

6 #89/603

I Have A Question For You
Issued: 1997 • Current
Original Price: $16
Market Value: $18.50

7 #97/724

I Love You
Issued: 1994 • Retired: 2000
Original Price: $15
Market Value: $17

8 #89/715

I Love You A Whole Bunch
Issued: 1997 • Current
Original Price: $17
Market Value: $18

CHARMING TAILS

	Price Paid	Value
1.		
2.		
3.		
4.		
5.		
6.		
7.		
8.		
Totals		

1 #89/756

I Miss You Already
Issued: 1999 • Current
Original Price: $17.50
Market Value: $17.50

2 #98/197

**I Picked This For You
(Event Piece)**
Issued: 1997 • Retired: 1998
Original Price: $18
Market Value: $50

3 #89/626

**I See Things
Clearly Now**
Issued: 1997 • Current
Original Price: $14
Market Value: $16

4 #89/719

I'm A Winner!
Issued: 1998 • Current
Original Price: $16
Market Value: $17

5 #89/706

I'm Here For You
Issued: 1998 • Current
Original Price: $17.50
Market Value: $18.50

6 #97/720

I'm So Sorry
Issued: 1994 • Retired: 1998
Original Price: $15
Market Value: $32

7 #89/701

I'm Thinking Of You
Issued: 1997 • Retired: 1999
Original Price: $15
Market Value: $27

8 #89/757

**In Every Life A Little
Rain Must Fall**
Issued: 1999 • Current
Original Price: $20
Market Value: $20

Charming Tails

	Price Paid	Value
1.		
2.		
3.		
4.		
5.		
6.		
7.		
8.		
Totals		

35

Figurines

1 #97/721

It's Not The Same Without You
Issued: 1994 • Retired: 1997
Original Price: $15
Market Value: $42

2 #89/704

It's Your Move
Issued: 1998 • Current
Original Price: $17
Market Value: $18

3 #89/627

Just Plane Friends
Issued: 1997 • Current
Original Price: $18
Market Value: $20

4 #89/710

Keeping Our Love Alive
Issued: 1997 • Current
Original Price: $19.50
Market Value: $20

5 #89/318

King Of The Mushroom
Issued: 1994 • Retired: 1996
Original Price: $16
Market Value: $50

6 #98/198

Life Is A Bed Of Roses (Event Piece)
Issued: 1998 • Retired: 1998
Original Price: $19
Market Value: $60

CHARMING TAILS

	Price Paid	Value
1.		
2.		
3.		
4.		
5.		
6.		
7.		
8.		
Totals		

7 #89/720

A Little Bird Told Me . . .
Issued: 1998 • Current
Original Price: $17
Market Value: $18

8 #87/862

Love Blooms (GCC Exclusive)
Issued: 1996 • Retired: 1997
Original Price: $16
Market Value: $53

Value Guide — CHARMING TAILS®

1 #87/395

Love Me – Love Me Not
Issued: 1996 • Retired: 1999
Original Price: $16
Market Value: $26

2 #89/314

Love Mice
Issued: 1994 • Retired: 1994
Original Price: $15
Market Value: $110

3 #89/604

Mackenzie Growing Beans
Issued: 1995 • Retired: 1995
Original Price: $15
Market Value: $56

4 #89/702

Maxine Goes On-Line
Issued: 1997 • Current
Original Price: $17
Market Value: $18

5 #98/460

Mender Of Broken Hearts
Issued: 1994 • Retired: 1996
Original Price: $15
Market Value: $48

6 #89/617

Midday Snooze
Issued: 1996 • Retired: 1999
Original Price: $18
Market Value: $26

7 #89/108

New!

Morning Hare
Issued: 2000 • Current
Original Price: $16
Market Value: $16

8 #89/321

Mouse On Grasshopper
Issued: 1994 • Retired: 1994
Original Price: $15
Market Value: $350

CHARMING TAILS

	Price Paid	Value
1.		
2.		
3.		
4.		
5.		
6.		
7.		
8.		

Totals

Figurines

1 #98/204

**My Spring Bonnet
(Parkwest/NALED
Exclusive)**
Issued: 1998 • Retired: 1999
Original Price: $18.50
Market Value: $42

2 #97/717

New Arrival
Issued: 1994 • Current
Original Price: $15
Market Value: $18

3 #89/758

**Now I Lay Me Down
To Sleep (LE-1999)**
Issued: 1999 • Closed: 1999
Original Price: $18
Market Value: $24

4 #87/360

One For Me . . .
Issued: 1996 • Retired: 1997
Original Price: $16
Market Value: $44

5 #87/361

One For You . . .
Issued: 1996 • Retired: 1997
Original Price: $16
Market Value: $40

6 #89/101

Party Animals
Issued: 1999 • Current
Original Price: $22
Market Value: $22

CHARMING TAILS

	Price Paid	Value
1.		
2.		
3.		
4.		
5.		
6.		
7.		
8.		
Totals		

7 #98/200

**Peek-A-Boo In
The Posies
(GCC Exclusive)**
Issued: 1998 • Retired: 1999
Original Price: $19.50
Market Value: $42

8 #89/722

Picture Perfect
Issued: 1998 • Current
Original Price: $17.50
Market Value: $18.50

Value Guide — CHARMING TAILS®

1 #97/718

Reach For The Stars
Issued: 1994 • Current
Original Price: $15
Market Value: $19

2 #98/207

Riding On The Wings Of Friendship (Event Piece)
Issued: 1998 • Retired: 1998
Original Price: $18
Market Value: $60

3 #89/560

Slumber Party
Issued: 1995 • Retired: 1996
Original Price: $16
Market Value: $68

4 #89/310

Spring Flowers
Issued: 1994 • Retired: 1996
Original Price: $16
Market Value: $60

5 #89/310

Spring Flowers
Issued: 1994 • Retired: 1996
Original Price: $16
Market Value: $65

6 #89/716

Steady Wins The Race (LE-1998)
Issued: 1998 • Closed: 1998
Original Price: $20
Market Value: $30

7 #87/353

Surrounded By Friends
Issued: 1996 • Retired: 1997
Original Price: $16
Market Value: $43

CHARMING TAILS

	Price Paid	Value
1.		
2.		
3.		
4.		
5.		
6.		
7.		

Totals

1   #87/399

Taggin' Along
Issued: 1996 • Retired: 1998
Original Price: $14
Market Value: $32

2   #87/691

**Take Me Home
(Event Piece)**
Issued: 1996 • Retired: 1996
Original Price: $17
Market Value: $70

3   #98/211

**Take Time To Notice
Those Around You
(Concepts Direct
Exclusive)**
Issued: 1999 • Retired: 1999
Original Price: $17.50
Market Value: $90

4   #87/396

Take Time To Reflect
Issued: 1996 • Retired: 1997
Original Price: $16
Market Value: $30

5   #89/765

**Take Time To Smell
The Flowers**
Issued: 1999 • Current
Original Price: $18
Market Value: $18

6   #89/103

**Take Two Aspirin And
Call Me In The Morning**
Issued: 1999 • Current
Original Price: $15
Market Value: $15

CHARMING TAILS

	Price Paid	Value
1.		
2.		
3.		
4.		
5.		
6.		
7.		
8.		

Totals

7   #89/700

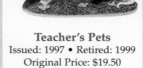

Teacher's Pets
Issued: 1997 • Retired: 1999
Original Price: $19.50
Market Value: $28

8   #89/754

Thanks For Being There
Issued: 1994 • Retired: 1996
Original Price: $15
Market Value: $52

1 #89/703

There's No "US" Without "U"
Issued: 1998 • Retired: 2000
Original Price: $19.50
Market Value: $28

2 #98/208

This One Is Yours (Event Piece)
Issued: 1999 • Retired: 1999
Original Price: $18
Market Value: N/E

3 #89/104

Together Every Step Of The Way
Issued: 1999 • Current
Original Price: $18
Market Value: $18

4 #87/398

Training Wings
Issued: 1996 • Retired: 1997
Original Price: $16
Market Value: $33

5 #87/362

Tuggin' Twosome (LE-10,000)
Issued: 1996 • Sold Out: 1996
Original Price: $18
Market Value: $53

6 #89/306

Two Peas In A Pod
Issued: 1994 • Retired: 1996
Original Price: $14
Market Value: $52

7 #89/111

New!

Wash Away Those Worries
Issued: 2000 • Current
Original Price: $17
Market Value: $17

8 #87/384

The Waterslide
Issued: 1996 • Current
Original Price: $20
Market Value: $22

CHARMING TAILS

	Price Paid	Value
1.		
2.		
3.		
4.		
5.		
6.		
7.		
8.		

Totals

1   #97/722

We'll Weather The Storm Together
Issued: 1994 • Current
Original Price: $15
Market Value: $18

2   #98/212

What's The Buzz? (GCC Exclusive)
Issued: 1999 • Retired: 1999
Original Price: $18
Market Value: N/E

3   #87/357

Why Hello There
Issued: 1996 • Retired: 1997
Original Price: $14
Market Value: $30

4   #98/930

Wishing You Well (Candlelighters Childhood Cancer Foundation Charity Piece)
Issued: 1999 • Current
Original Price: $20
Market Value: $20

5   #89/2000

A World Of Good Wishes (LE-2000)
Issued: 1999 • Closed: 2000
Original Price: $24
Market Value: $28

6   #98/929

You Are Not Alone (AMFAR Charity Piece)
Issued: 1995 • Retired: 1996
Original Price: $20
Market Value: $52

CHARMING TAILS

	Price Paid	Value
1.		
2.		
3.		
4.		
5.		
6.		
7.		
8.		

Totals

7   #89/625

You Couldn't Be Sweeter
Issued: 1997 • Current
Original Price: $16
Market Value: $18

8   #89/105

You Quack Me Up
Issued: 1999 • Current
Original Price: $18
Market Value: $18

Value Guide — CHARMING TAILS®

1   #89/762

You're My Cup Of Tea
Issued: 1999 • Current
Original Price: $19
Market Value: $19

2   #87/372

After The Hunt
Issued: 1996 • Current
Original Price: $18
Market Value: $19

3   #87/422

**Binkey's Bouncing
Bundle (LE-7,500)**
Issued: 1996 • Sold Out: 1996
Original Price: $18
Market Value: $60

4   #89/609

Bunny Impostor
Issued: 1995 • Retired: 1998
Original Price: $12
Market Value: $26

5   #87/424

Bunny Love
Issued: 1996 • Current
Original Price: $18
Market Value: $19

6   #88/700

Chickie Back Ride
Issued: 1998 • Current
Original Price: $15
Market Value: $15

7   #88/100

New!

Chickie Chariot Ride
Issued: 2000 • Current
Original Price: $18
Market Value: $18

CHARMING TAILS

	Price Paid	Value
1.		

EASTER

2.		
3.		
4.		
5.		
6.		
7.		

Totals   43

1   #89/316

Duckling In Egg W/Mouse
Issued: 1994 • Retired: 1994
Original Price: $15
Market Value: $380

2   #88/101

New!

Ducky Weather
Issued: 2000 • Current
Original Price: $18
Market Value: $18

3   #87/377

Gathering Treats
Issued: 1996 • Retired: 1998
Original Price: $12
Market Value: $26

4   #89/559

Jelly Bean Feast
Issued: 1995 • Retired: 1996
Original Price: $14
Market Value: $43

5   #87/373

Look Out Below
Issued: 1996 • Retired: 1997
Original Price: $20
Market Value: $45

6   #88/703

Motoring Along
Issued: 1999 • Current
Original Price: $16.50
Market Value: $16.50

7   #88/603

No Thanks, I'm Stuffed
Issued: 1997 • Current
Original Price: $15
Market Value: $16

8   #88/701

Paint-By-Paws
Issued: 1998 • Current
Original Price: $16
Market Value: $16

EASTER

	Price Paid	Value
1.		
2.		
3.		
4.		
5.		
6.		
7.		
8.		

Totals

44

Value Guide — CHARMING TAILS®

1 #88/702

Shhh, Don't Make A Peep
Issued: 1999 • Current
Original Price: $16.50
Market Value: $16.50

2 #89/561

Wanna Play? (LE-2,500)
Issued: 1995 • Sold Out: 1995
Original Price: $15
Market Value: $155

3 #87/379

Want A Bite?
Issued: 1996 • Retired: 1997
Original Price: $18
Market Value: $42

4 #88/600

What's Hatchin'?
Issued: 1997 • Current
Original Price: $16
Market Value: $17

5 #84/107

New!

An Abundance Of Love
Issued: 2000 • Current
Original Price: $18
Market Value: $18

6 #84/108

New!

Candy Kisses
Issued: 2000 • Current
Original Price: $17
Market Value: $17

7 #84/109

New!

Give Love A Shot!
Issued: 2000 • Current
Original Price: $15
Market Value: $15

8 #84/106

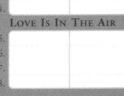

I'd Do It All Over Again
Issued: 1999 • Current
Original Price: $17.50
Market Value: $17.50

EASTER	
Price Paid	Value
1.	
2.	
3.	
4.	

LOVE IS IN THE AIR	
5.	
6.	
7.	
8.	

Totals

1 #84/101

I'm Your Love Bunny
Issued: 1999 • Current
Original Price: $16
Market Value: $16

2 New! #84/110

Love Birds
Issued: 2000 • Current
Original Price: $20
Market Value: $20

3 #84/100

Love Is In The Air
Issued: 1999 • Current
Original Price: $19.50
Market Value: $19.50

4 #84/103

Our Love Has Blossomed
Issued: 1999 • Current
Original Price: $18
Market Value: $18

5 New! #84/111

We're A Perfect Fit
Issued: 2000 • Current
Original Price: $17
Market Value: $17

6 #84/104

You Can't Run From Love
Issued: 1999 • Current
Original Price: $17.50
Market Value: $17.50

LOVE IS IN THE AIR

	Price Paid	Value
1.		
2.		
3.		
4.		
5.		
6.		

THE WEDDING

7.		
8.		

Totals

7 #82/108

The Altar Of Love
Issued: 1998 • Current
Original Price: $25
Market Value: $25

8 #82/103

The Best . . . Bunny
Issued: 1998 • Current
Original Price: $16
Market Value: $16.50

Value Guide — CHARMING TAILS®

1 #82/107

The Get-Away Car
Issued: 1998 • Current
Original Price: $22
Market Value: $23

2 #82/100

Here Comes The Bride
Issued: 1998 • Current
Original Price: $17
Market Value: $17.50

3 #82/102

Maid Of Honor
Issued: 1998 • Current
Original Price: $16
Market Value: $16.50

4 #82/101

My Heart's All A-Flutter
Issued: 1998 • Current
Original Price: $17
Market Value: $17.50

5 #82/104

The Ring Bearer
Issued: 1998 • Current
Original Price: $16
Market Value: $16.50

6 #82/109

Together Forever
Issued: 1998 • Current
Original Price: $25
Market Value: $26

7 #82/105

Wedding Day Blossoms
Issued: 1998 • Current
Original Price: $16
Market Value: $16.50

8 #83/100

New!

Adventure Bound
Issued: 2000 • Current
Original Price: $20
Market Value: $20

THE WEDDING

	Price Paid	Value
1.		
2.		
3.		
4.		
5.		
6.		
7.		

LAZY DAYS

8.		

Totals

47

1 #83/101

New!

Beach Bunnie
Issued: 2000 • Current
Original Price: $16
Market Value: $16

2 #83/704

The Blossom Bounce
Issued: 1997 • Retired: 1999
Original Price: $20
Market Value: $30

3 #83/802

Building Castles
Issued: 1997 • Retired: 1999
Original Price: $17
Market Value: $28

4 #83/806

Buried Treasures
Issued: 1999 • Current
Original Price: $19
Market Value: $19

5 #83/703

Camping Out
Issued: 1998 • Current
Original Price: $18.50
Market Value: $19.50

6 #83/102

New!

Catching Fireflies
Issued: 2000 • Current
Original Price: $18
Market Value: $18

LAZY DAYS

	Price Paid	Value
1.		
2.		
3.		
4.		
5.		
6.		
7.		
8.		

Totals

7 #83/804

Come On In – The Water's Fine!
Issued: 1998 • Current
Original Price: $18
Market Value: $18.50

8 #83/803

A Day At The Lake
Issued: 1998 • Current
Original Price: $18.50
Market Value: $19

1	#83/810

**Friendship Is Always A
Great Bargain**
Issued: 1999 • Current
Original Price: $19.50
Market Value: $19.50

2	#83/702

Gone Fishin'
Issued: 1997 • Retired: 1999
Original Price: $16
Market Value: $28

3	#83/103

New!

Hang Ten
Issued: 2000 • Current
Original Price: $19
Market Value: $19

4	#83/701

Life's A Picnic With You
Issued: 1997 • Retired: 1999
Original Price: $18
Market Value: $28

5	#83/809

**Mow, Mow, Mow
The Lawn**
Issued: 1999 • Current
Original Price: $16.50
Market Value: $16.50

6	#83/104

New!

A Real Lifesaver
Issued: 2000 • Current
Original Price: $20
Market Value: $20

7	#83/801

Rowboat Romance
Issued: 1997 • Current
Original Price: $15.50
Market Value: $17

LAZY DAYS

	Price Paid	Value
1.		
2.		
3.		
4.		
5.		
6.		
7.		
	Totals	

Figurines

1 #83/805

**Stewart's Day
In The Sun**
Issued: 1998 • Current
Original Price: $17
Market Value: $17.50

2 #83/700

Toasting Marshmallows
Issued: 1998 • Current
Original Price: $20
Market Value: $21

3 #83/807

Triple Delight
Issued: 1999 • Current
Original Price: $18
Market Value: $18

4 #85/501

New!

Autumn Breezes
Issued: 2000 • Current
Original Price: $17
Market Value: $17

5 #87/436

**Bag Of Tricks . . .
Or Treats**
Issued: 1996 • Current
Original Price: $15.50
Market Value: $18

6 #85/500

New!

Be Thankful For Friends
Issued: 2000 • Current
Original Price: $20
Market Value: $20

7 #87/429

Binkey's Acorn Costume
Issued: 1996 • Retired: 2000
Original Price: $11.50
Market Value: $13.50

LAZY DAYS

	Price Paid	Value
1.		
2.		
3.		

HALLOWEEN/
AUTUMN HARVEST

4.		
5.		
6.		
7.		

Totals

1 #85/417

Boooo!
Issued: 1998 • Current
Original Price: $18
Market Value: $19

2 #85/611

Candy Apples
Issued: 1995 • Retired: 1998
Original Price: $16
Market Value: $33

3 #85/607

Candy Corn Vampire
Issued: 1995 • Retired: 1997
Original Price: $18
Market Value: $50

4 #85/402

Caps Off To You
Issued: 1993 • Retired: 1996
Original Price: $10
Market Value: $44

5 #87/431

Chauncey's Pear Costume
Issued: 1996 • Retired: 1998
Original Price: $12
Market Value: $28

6 #85/399

Cornfield Feast
Issued: 1993 • Retired: 1994
Original Price: $15
Market Value: $160

7 #85/401

Fall Frolicking
Issued: 1993 • Retired: 1996
Original Price: $13
Market Value: $55

8 #85/401

Fall Frolicking
Issued: 1993 • Retired: 1996
Original Price: $13
Market Value: $55

HALLOWEEN/ AUTUMN HARVEST	
Price Paid	Value
1.	
2.	
3.	
4.	
5.	
6.	
7.	
8.	
Totals	

Figurines

1 #85/511

Frosting Pumpkins
Issued: 1994 • Retired: 1996
Original Price: $16
Market Value: $46

2 #85/615

Garden Naptime
Issued: 1995 • Retired: 1997
Original Price: $18
Market Value: $42

3 #85/703

Ghost Stories
Issued: 1997 • Current
Original Price: $18.50
Market Value: $20

4 #85/608

Giving Thanks
(GCC Early Release)
Issued: 1995 • Current
Original Price: $16
Market Value: $19

5 #85/704

The Good Witch
Issued: 1997 • Current
Original Price: $18.50
Market Value: $20

6 #85/398

Gourd Slide
Issued: 1993 • Retired: 1996
Original Price: $16
Market Value: $56

HALLOWEEN/ AUTUMN HARVEST	
Price Paid	Value
1.	
2.	
3.	
4.	
5.	
6.	
7.	
8.	
Totals	

7 #85/507

Harvest Fruit
Issued: 1994 • Retired: 1995
Original Price: $16
Market Value: $60

8 #85/507

Harvest Fruit
Issued: 1994 • Retired: 1995
Original Price: $16
Market Value: $56

1   #85/882

Harvest Time Honeys
Issued: 1999 • Current
Original Price: $18.50
Market Value: $18.50

2   #85/883

Haunted Hayride
Issued: 1999 • Current
Original Price: $18.50
Market Value: $18.50

3   #85/880

Hocus Pocus
Issued: 1999 • Current
Original Price: $18
Market Value: $18

4   #85/610

Horn Of Plenty
Issued: 1995 • Retired: 1997
Original Price: $20
Market Value: $42

5   #87/446

Indian Impostor
Issued: 1996 • Current
Original Price: $14
Market Value: $16

6   #85/410

Jack O'Lantern Jalopy
Issued: 1998 • Current
Original Price: $18
Market Value: $18.50

7   #85/512

Jumpin' Jack O'Lantern
Issued: 1994 • Retired: 1997
Original Price: $16
Market Value: $42

HALLOWEEN/ AUTUMN HARVEST		
	Price Paid	Value
1.		
2.		
3.		
4.		
5.		
6.		
7.		
	Totals	

Figurines

1   #85/776

Let's Get Crackin'
Issued: 1995 • Retired: 1997
Original Price: $20
Market Value: $46

2   #87/428

Look! No Hands
Issued: 1996 • Retired: 1999
Original Price: $15.50
Market Value: $28

3   #85/881

Mackenzie's Putt-Putt Tractor
Issued: 1999 • Current
Original Price: $17.50
Market Value: $17.50

4   #87/430

Maxine's Pumpkin Costume
Issued: 1996 • Current
Original Price: $12
Market Value: $15

5   #87/443

Oops! I Missed
Issued: 1996 • Retired: 1998
Original Price: $16
Market Value: $30

6   #85/508

Open Pumpkin
Issued: 1994 • Retired: 1994
Original Price: $15
Market Value: $90

HALLOWEEN/ AUTUMN HARVEST

	Price Paid	Value
1.		
2.		
3.		
4.		
5.		
6.		
7.		
8.		

Totals

7   #85/514

Painting Leaves
Issued: 1994 • Retired: 1996
Original Price: $16
Market Value: $46

8   #87/438

Pickin' Time
Issued: 1996 • Retired: 1997
Original Price: $16
Market Value: $34

Value Guide — CHARMING TAILS®

1   #87/445

Pilgrim's Progress
Issued: 1996 • Current
Original Price: $13.50
Market Value: $15

2   #85/606

**Pumpkin Pie
(GCC Early Release)**
Issued: 1995 • Retired: 1996
Original Price: $16
Market Value: $52

3   #85/513

Pumpkin Slide
Issued: 1994 • Retired: 1995
Original Price: $16
Market Value: $55

4   #85/411

Pumpkin's First Pumpkin
Issued: 1998 • Current
Original Price: $17
Market Value: $18

5   #85/100

New!

Put On A Happy Face
Issued: 2000 • Current
Original Price: $17
Market Value: $17

6   #85/701

**Reginald's Gourd
Costume**
Issued: 1997 • Retired: 2000
Original Price: $12.50
Market Value: $13.50

7   #85/777

Reginald's Hideaway
Issued: 1995 • Retired: 1997
Original Price: $14
Market Value: $38

8   #85/416

Stack O'Lanterns
Issued: 1998 • Current
Original Price: $18
Market Value: $18.50

HALLOWEEN/ AUTUMN HARVEST		
	Price Paid	Value
1.		
2.		
3.		
4.		
5.		
6.		
7.		
8.		

Totals

Figurines

1 #85/700

Stewart's Apple Costume
Issued: 1997 • Retired: 2000
Original Price: $12.50
Market Value: $13.50

2 #85/702

Turkey Traveller
Issued: 1997 • Current
Original Price: $18.50
Market Value: $20

3 #85/412

Turkey With Dressing
Issued: 1998 • Current
Original Price: $18
Market Value: $19

4 #85/101

New!

What A Hoot!
Issued: 2000 • Current
Original Price: $17
Market Value: $17

5 #87/440

You're Not Scary
Issued: 1996 • Retired: 1998
Original Price: $14
Market Value: $30

6 #87/451

You're Nutty
Issued: 1996 • Retired: 1998
Original Price: $12
Market Value: $28

7 #87/698

Airmail
Issued: 1996 • Retired: 1997
Original Price: $16
Market Value: $34

8 #87/498

All I Can Give You Is Me
(GCC Early Release)
Issued: 1996 • Retired: 1997
Original Price: $15
Market Value: $48

HALLOWEEN/ AUTUMN HARVEST	
Price Paid	Value
1.	
2.	
3.	
4.	
5.	
6.	
SQUASHVILLE	
7.	
8.	

Totals

1 #87/703

**All The Trimmings
(LE-1997)**
Issued: 1997 • Closed: 1997
Original Price: $15
Market Value: $32

2 #87/705

**Baby's First Christmas
(1st Edition, Dated 1997)**
Baby's First
Issued: 1997 • Closed: 1997
Original Price: $18.50
Market Value: $26

3 #87/600

**Bearing Gifts
(GCC Early Release)**
Issued: 1997 • Current
Original Price: $16
Market Value: $16.50

4 #87/426

**Binkey In A
Bed Of Flowers
(GCC Early Release)**
Issued: 1996 • Retired: 1996
Original Price: $15
Market Value: $44

5 #87/580

Binkey Snowshoeing
Issued: 1995 • Current
Original Price: $14
Market Value: $16

6 #87/572

**Binkey's 1995
Ice Sculpture (LE-1995)**
Issued: 1995 • Closed: 1995
Original Price: $20
Market Value: $40

7 #87/692

Building A Snowbunny
Issued: 1996 • Current
Original Price: $16
Market Value: $18

8 #87/619

**Building Blocks Of
Christmas
(2nd Edition, Dated 1998)**
Baby's First
Issued: 1998 • Closed: 1998
Original Price: $17
Market Value: $22

SQUASHVILLE

	Price Paid	Value
1.		
2.		
3.		
4.		
5.		
6.		
7.		
8.		

Totals

Figurines

1 #87/575

Christmas Stroll
Issued: 1996 • Current
Original Price: $16
Market Value: $18

2 #87/112

Christmas Tree Trio
(Fifth Avenue Exclusive)
Issued: 1999 • Retired: 1999
Original Price: $20
Market Value: $40

3 #87/713

Christmas Trio
Issued: 1997 • Current
Original Price: $15.50
Market Value: $17.50

4 #87/624

Dashing Through
The Snow
Issued: 1998 • Current
Original Price: $16.50
Market Value: $17.50

5 #87/714

Decorating Binkey
Issued: 1997 • Current
Original Price: $16
Market Value: $17.50

6 #87/208

New!

Dive Into The Holidays
Issued: 2000 • Current
Original Price: $22
Market Value: $22

SQUASHVILLE

	Price Paid	Value
1.		
2.		
3.		
4.		
5.		
6.		
7.		
Totals		

7 #98/215

Earrings Too Much?
(GCC Exclusive)
Issued: 1999 • Retired: 1999
Original Price: $16.50
Market Value: $35

1   #87/102

Everybody Sing
Issued: 1999 • Current
Original Price: $26
Market Value: $26

2   #87/590

Extra! Extra!
Issued: 1996 • Retired: 1997
Original Price: $14
Market Value: $35

3   #87/695

Farmer Mackenzie
Issued: 1996 • Current
Original Price: $16
Market Value: $17.50

4   #87/305

Flying Leaf Saucer
Issued: 1995 • Current
Original Price: $16
Market Value: $18

5   #87/473

Follow In My Footsteps
Issued: 1996 • Retired: 2000
Original Price: $12
Market Value: $14

6   #98/214

Follow The Star
(Parkwest/NALED
Exclusive)
Issued: 1999 • Retired: 1999
Original Price: $22
Market Value: $44

7   #87/993

Hot Doggin'
Issued: 1994 • Retired: 1995
Original Price: $20
Market Value: $50

8   #87/513

Jingle Bells
Issued: 1996 • Retired: 1997
Original Price: $15
Market Value: $35

SQUASHVILLE

	Price Paid	Value
1.		
2.		
3.		
4.		
5.		
6.		
7.		
8.		

Totals

Figurines

1   #87/209

New!

Just The Right Size
Issued: 2000 • Current
Original Price: $20
Market Value: $20

2   #87/205

New!

**Kiss-Mas Lights
(LE-2000)**
Issued: 2000 • Current
Original Price: $19
Market Value: $19

3   #87/188

Lady Bug Express
Issued: 1994 • Retired: 1994
Original Price: $18
Market Value: $250

4   #87/207

New!

**The Littlest Reindeer
(4th Edition, Dated 2000)**
Baby's First
Issued: 2000 • Current
Original Price: $17
Market Value: $17

5   #87/925

**Mackenzie & Maxine
Caroling**
Issued: 1994 • Retired: 1995
Original Price: $18
Market Value: $42

6   #87/203

**Mackenzie Building A
Snowmouse (LE-7,500)**
Issued: 1994 • Sold Out: 1994
Original Price: $18
Market Value: $140

7   #98/196

**Mackenzie The
Snowman
(Parkwest/NALED
Exclusive)**
Issued: 1997 • Retired: 1998
Original Price: $17
Market Value: $46

8   #98/202

**Mackenzie's Holiday Hat
(Parkwest/NALED
Exclusive)**
Issued: 1998 • Retired: 1998
Original Price: $17
Market Value: $60

Squashville

	Price Paid	Value
1.		
2.		
3.		
4.		
5.		
6.		
7.		
8.		

Totals

Value Guide — Charming Tails®

1   #98/201

**Mackenzie's Wish List
(GCC Exclusive)**
Issued: 1998 • Retired: 1998
Original Price: $17
Market Value: $50

2   #87/573

Mail Mouse
Issued: 1995 • Retired: 1996
Original Price: $12
Market Value: $40

3   #87/510

**Maxine Making
Snow Angels**
Issued: 1994 • Current
Original Price: $20
Market Value: $21.50

4   #98/216

**Maxine's Snowcap
(Concepts Direct
Exclusive)**
Issued: 1999 • Retired: 1999
Original Price: $18
Market Value: $35

5   #87/612

**Maxine's Snowmobile
Ride (Parkwest/NALED
Early Release)**
Issued: 1997 • Current
Original Price: $17
Market Value: $18

6   #87/622

**Merry Christmas From
Our House To Yours**
Issued: 1998 • Current
Original Price: $23
Market Value: $24

7   #87/206

New!

My Little Chick-A-Deer
Issued: 2000 • Current
Original Price: $18
Market Value: $18

8   #87/500

My New Toy
Issued: 1996 • Retired: 1997
Original Price: $14
Market Value: $28

Squashville

	Price Paid	Value
1.		
2.		
3.		
4.		
5.		
6.		
7.		
8.		

Totals

Figurines

1 #87/101

Nestled In For The Holidays
Issued: 1999 • Current
Original Price: $20
Market Value: $20

2 #87/111

New Decorations (3rd Edition, Dated 1999)
Baby's First
Issued: 1999 • Closed: 1999
Original Price: $16.50
Market Value: N/E

3 #87/704

Not A Creature Was Stirring
Issued: 1997 • Current
Original Price: $17
Market Value: $18

4 #87/213

New!

Oh Mackenzie Tree . . .
Issued: 2000 • Current
Original Price: $17
Market Value: $17

5 #98/210

On The First Day Of Christmas (Event Piece)
Issued: 1999 • Retired: 1999
Original Price: $17.50
Market Value: N/E

6 #98/195

A One Mouse Open Sleigh (GCC Exclusive)
Issued: 1997 • Retired: 1998
Original Price: $17
Market Value: $40

SQUASHVILLE

	Price Paid	Value
1.		
2.		
3.		
4.		
5.		
6.		
7.		
Totals		

7 #87/469

OOPS! Did I Do That?
Issued: 1996 • Retired: 1997
Original Price: $14
Market Value: $28

1   #87/565

Pear Taxi
Issued: 1995 • Retired: 1996
Original Price: $16
Market Value: $42

2   #87/527

Peeking At Presents
Issued: 1996 • Retired: 1997
Original Price: $13
Market Value: $28

3   #87/625

Please, Just One More . . .
Issued: 1998 • Current
Original Price: $16.50
Market Value: $17.50

4   #87/591

Reginald's Newsstand
Issued: 1996 • Retired: 1997
Original Price: $20
Market Value: $32

5   #87/601

Sending A Little Snow Your Way (GCC Exclusive)
Issued: 1996 • Retired: 1997
Original Price: $15
Market Value: $50

6   #87/204

New!

A Shoveling We Will Go
Issued: 2000 • Current
Original Price: $18
Market Value: $18

7   #87/103

Skating Party
Issued: 1999 • Current
Original Price: $21
Market Value: $21

8   #87/569

Sleigh Ride (LE-7,500)
Issued: 1995 • Sold Out: 1995
Original Price: $16
Market Value: $95

SQUASHVILLE

	Price Paid	Value
1.		
2.		
3.		
4.		
5.		
6.		
7.		
8.		

Totals

Figurines

1   #87/100

Sleighride Sweeties (LE-1999)
Issued: 1999 • Closed: 1999
Original Price: $23
Market Value: $55

2   #87/512

Snack For The Reindeer
Issued: 1996 • Retired: 1996
Original Price: $13
Market Value: $45

3   #87/566

Snow Plow
Issued: 1995 • Current
Original Price: $16
Market Value: $18

4   #87/570

The Snowball Fight
Issued: 1995 • Retired: 1999
Original Price: $16
Market Value: $26

5   #87/113

Snowshoe Sweetie (Simply Christmas Exclusive)
Issued: 1999 • Retired: 1999
Original Price: $17
Market Value: $35

6   #98/209

Stack-O-Sweeties (Concepts Direct Exclusive)
Issued: 1999 • Retired: 1999
Original Price: $17
Market Value: $45

SQUASHVILLE

	Price Paid	Value
1.		
2.		
3.		
4.		
5.		
6.		
7.		
8.		
Totals		

7   #87/110

The Stockings Were Hung By The Chimney
Issued: 1999 • Current
Original Price: $18.50
Market Value: $18.50

8   #87/623

Team Igloo (LE-1998)
Issued: 1998 • Closed: 1998
Original Price: $23
Market Value: $32

Value Guide — CHARMING TAILS®

1   #87/571

Teamwork Helps!
Issued: 1995 • Current
Original Price: $16
Market Value: $17.50

2   #87/514

Testing The Lights
Issued: 1996 • Retired: 1997
Original Price: $14
Market Value: $32

3   #87/702

**Trimming The Tree
(set/2)**
Issued: 1997 • Current
Original Price: $27.50
Market Value: $28

4   #87/496

**Waiting For Christmas
(LE-14,000)**
Issued: 1996 • Sold Out: 1996
Original Price: $16
Market Value: $52

5   #87/621

**Who Put That
Tree There?**
Issued: 1998 • Current
Original Price: $16.50
Market Value: $17.50

6   #87/114

**Winter Whirl-Wind
(G & L Christmas
Barn Exclusive)**
Issued: 1999 • Retired: 1999
Original Price: $20
Market Value: $45

7   #87/472

You Melted My Heart
Issued: 1996 • Retired: 1998
Original Price: $20
Market Value: $40

8   #87/481

Angel Of Light
Issued: 1996 • Current
Original Price: $12
Market Value: $14

SQUASHVILLE

	Price Paid	Value
1.		
2.		
3.		
4.		
5.		
6.		
7.		

SQUASHVILLE CHRISTMAS PAGEANT

8.		

Totals

Figurines

1 #87/546

Christmas Pageant Stage
Issued: 1995 • Current
Original Price: $30
Market Value: $32

2 #87/547

Holy Family Players (set/3)
Issued: 1995 • Current
Original Price: $20
Market Value: $22

3 #87/480

L'il Drummer Mouse
Issued: 1996 • Current
Original Price: $12
Market Value: $14

4 #87/482

Manger Animals (set/4)
Issued: 1996 • Current
Original Price: $20
Market Value: $22

5 #87/710

Squashville Shepherds (set/2)
Issued: 1997 • Current
Original Price: $12.50
Market Value: $13.50

6 #87/548

Three Wise Mice (set/3)
Issued: 1995 • Current
Original Price: $20
Market Value: $22

SQUASHVILLE CHRISTMAS PAGEANT

	Price Paid	Value
1.		
2.		
3.		
4.		
5.		
6.		

SQUASHVILLE CHRISTMAS PARADE

7.		
8.		

Totals

7 #87/554

Chauncey's Noisemakers
Issued: 1996 • Current
Original Price: $12
Market Value: $13.50

8 #87/556

The Drum Major
Issued: 1996 • Current
Original Price: $12
Market Value: $13.50

66

Figurines

1 #87/587

The Float Driver
Issued: 1996 • Current
Original Price: $12
Market Value: $13.50

2 #87/555

Holiday Trumpeter
Issued: 1996 • Current
Original Price: $12
Market Value: $13.50

3 #87/557

Little Drummer Boy
Issued: 1996 • Current
Original Price: $12
Market Value: $13.50

4 #87/576

Mackenzie Claus
On Parade
Issued: 1996 • Current
Original Price: $22
Market Value: $24

5 #87/543

Parade Banner
Issued: 1996 • Current
Original Price: $16
Market Value: $18

6 #87/708

The Santa Balloon
Issued: 1997 • Current
Original Price: $25
Market Value: $26

7 #87/626

Snowman Float
Issued: 1998 • Current
Original Price: $25
Market Value: $25

SQUASHVILLE CHRISTMAS PARADE

	Price Paid	Value
1.		
2.		
3.		
4.		
5.	12	13
6.	15	26
7.		
Totals		

Figurines

1 #87/104

Sugar Time Band Float
Issued: 1999 • Current
Original Price: $25
Market Value: $25

2 #87/696

Town Crier
Issued: 1996 • Current
Original Price: $14
Market Value: $16

3 #87/579

Charming Choo-Choo And Passenger (set/2)
Issued: 1995 • Retired: 1999
Original Price: $35
Market Value: $44

4 #87/707

Chauncey's Choo-Choo Ride
Issued: 1997 • Retired: 1999
Original Price: $19
Market Value: $23

5 #87/620

Reginald's Choo-Choo Ride
Issued: 1998 • Retired: 1999
Original Price: $19
Market Value: $22

6 #87/694

Stewart's Choo-Choo Ride
Issued: 1996 • Retired: 1999
Original Price: $17.50
Market Value: $24

| SQUASHVILLE CHRISTMAS PARADE | |
Price Paid	Value
1.	
2.	
CHARMING CHOO-CHOO	
3.	
4.	
5.	
6.	
7.	
8.	
Totals	

7 #87/105

Tea Party Train Ride
Issued: 1999 • Retired: 1999
Original Price: $26
Market Value: $28

8 #87/210

New!

Wait For Us! (LE-2000)
Issued: 2000 • Current
Original Price: $20
Market Value: $20

Value Guide — CHARMING TAILS®

1 #87/948

Acorn Street Lamp
Issued: 1994 • Retired: 1997
Original Price: $5
Market Value: $18

2 #87/562

**Butternut Squash Dairy
(lighted, LE-7,500)**
Issued: 1995 • Sold Out: 1996
Original Price: $45
Market Value: $90

3 #87/611

**Candy Apple Store
(lighted, LE-9,000)**
Issued: 1996 • Sold Out: 1997
Original Price: $45
Market Value: $90

4 #87/597

**Cantaloupe Cathedral
(lighted)**
Issued: 1996 • Retired: 1997
Original Price: $45
Market Value: $55

5 #87/583

**Carrot Post Office
(lighted)**
Issued: 1995 • Retired: 1996
Original Price: $45
Market Value: $88

6 #87/521

**Chestnut Chapel
(lighted)**
Issued: 1994 • Retired: 1996
Original Price: $45
Market Value: $99

7 #87/584

**Great Oak Tow___ ____all
(lighted____**
Issued: 1995 • Retired: __997
Original Price: $45
Market Value: $75

8 #87/947

Leaf Fence
Issued: 1994 • Retired: 1997
Original Price: $6
Market Value: $20

SQUASHVILLE VILLAGE

	Price Paid	Value
1.		
2.		
3.		
4.		
5.		
6.		
7.		
8.		
Totals		

1   #87/560

Mail Box & Bench
Issued: 1995 • Retired: 1995
Original Price: $11
Market Value: $20

2   #87/563

Mushroom Depot (lighted)
Issued: 1995 • Retired: 1997
Original Price: $45
Market Value: $70

3   #87/524

Old Cob Mill (lighted, LE-7,500)
Issued: 1994 • Sold Out: 1996
Original Price: $45
Market Value: $98

4   #87/522

Pumpkin Inn (lighted)
Issued: 1994 • Retired: 1997
Original Price: $45
Market Value: $80

5   #87/561

Street Light & Sign
Issued: 1995 • Retired: 1997
Original Price: $11
Market Value: $25

6   #87/533

Village Sign Accessory
Issued: 1994 • Current
Original Price: $30
Market Value: $33

SQUASHVILLE VILLAGE

	Price Paid	Value
1.		
2.		
3.		
4.		
5.		
6.		

Totals

CHARMING TAILS® ORNAMENTS

The Charming Tails collection got its start as a small line of Christmas ornaments. While the main focus of the line has since become figurines, several ornaments are still released every year to help collectors celebrate the holidays. Ornaments are divided into three major categories: "Charming Tails," "Easter" and "Deck The Halls." Six new ornaments join the collection in 2000, all part of the "Deck The Halls" collection.

1 #89/752

Binkey In The Berry Patch
Issued: 1995 • Retired: 1996
Original Price: $12
Market Value: $60

2 #87/367

Hello, Sweet Pea
Issued: 1996 • Retired: 1997
Original Price: $12
Market Value: $33

3 #87/390

I'm Berry Happy
Issued: 1996 • Retired: 1997
Original Price: $15
Market Value: $39

4 #87/365

I'm Full
Issued: 1996 • Retired: 1997
Original Price: $15
Market Value: $36

5 #89/190

Maxine's Butterfly Ride
Issued: 1994 • Current
Original Price: $16.50
Market Value: $18

6 #89/562

**Mouse In Strawberry
(GCC Early Release)**
Issued: 1995 • Retired: 1995
Original Price: $12
Market Value: $64

	CHARMING TAILS	
	Price Paid	Value
1.		
2.		
3.		
4.		
5.		
6.		
	Totals	

1 #89/191

Mouse On Bee
Issued: 1994 • Retired: 1994
Original Price: $16.50
Market Value: $325

2 #89/320

Mouse On Dragonfly
Issued: 1994 • Retired: 1994
Original Price: $16.50
Market Value: $415

3 #87/369

Picking Peppers
Issued: 1996 • Retired: 1997
Original Price: $12
Market Value: $32

4 #89/563

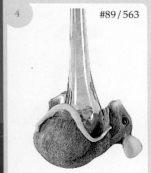

Springtime Showers
Issued: 1995 • Retired: 1996
Original Price: $10
Market Value: $54

5 #89/563

Springtime Showers
Issued: 1995 • Retired: 1996
Original Price: $10
Market Value: $54

6 #89/563

Springtime Showers
Issued: 1995 • Retired: 1996
Original Price: $10
Market Value: $54

Charming Tails

Price Paid	Value
1.	
2.	
3.	
4.	
5.	
6.	
7.	

Easter
8.	

Totals

7 #87/366

This Is Hot!
Issued: 1996 • Retired: 1997
Original Price: $15
Market Value: $32

8 #89/313

Animals In Eggs
Issued: 1994 • Retired: 1996
Original Price: $11
Market Value: $48

1   #89/313

Animals In Eggs
Issued: 1994 • Retired: 1996
Original Price: $11
Market Value: $48

2   #89/313

Animals In Eggs
Issued: 1994 • Retired: 1996
Original Price: $11
Market Value: $48

3   #89/313

Animals In Eggs
Issued: 1994 • Retired: 1996
Original Price: $11
Market Value: $48

4   #89/615

Easter Parade
Issued: 1995 • Retired: 1996
Original Price: $10
Market Value: $40

5   #89/753

Peek-A-Boo!
Issued: 1995 • Retired: 1996
Original Price: $12
Market Value: $36

6   #87/306

**1995 Annual Ornament
(Dated 1995)**
Issued: 1995 • Closed: 1995
Original Price: $16
Market Value: $35

7   #87/850

**1996 Baby's First
Christmas (2nd Edition)**
Baby's First
Issued: 1996 • Closed: 1996
Original Price: $13
Market Value: $36

8   #86/100

New!

**2000 Snowflakes
(Dated 2000)**
Issued: 2000 • Current
Original Price: $11.50
Market Value: $11.50

EASTER	Price Paid	Value
1.		
2.		
3.		
4.		
5.		
DECK THE HALLS		
6.		
7.		
8.		
Totals		

73

Value Guide — CHARMING TAILS®

1   #86/652

Air Mail To Santa
Issued: 1998 • Current
Original Price: $13
Market Value: $13

2   #86/660

All Lit Up
Issued: 1997 • Current
Original Price: $11
Market Value: $13

3   #87/471

All Wrapped Up
(Dated 1996)
Issued: 1996 • Closed: 1996
Original Price: $12
Market Value: $42

4   #87/032

Apple House (lighted)
Issued: 1994 • Retired: 1995
Original Price: $13
Market Value: $75

5   #87/184

Baby's First Christmas
(1st Edition)
Baby's First
Issued: 1994 • Closed: 1994
Original Price: $12
Market Value: $45

6   #86/792

Baby's First Christmas
(5th Edition)
Baby's First
Issued: 1999 • Closed: 1999
Original Price: $11.50
Market Value: N/E

DECK THE HALLS

	Price Paid	Value
1.		
2.		
3.		
4.		
5.		
6.		
7.		
8.		

7   #87/924

Binkey & Reginald
On Ice
Issued: 1994 • Retired: 1994
Original Price: $10
Market Value: $200

8   #87/924

Binkey & Reginald
On Ice
Issued: 1994 • Retired: 1994
Original Price: $10
Market Value: $200

1   #86/793

**Binkey's Candy
Cane Flyer**
Issued: 1999 • Current
Original Price: $11.50
Market Value: $11.50

2   #87/303

Binkey's Poinsettia
Issued: 1995 • Retired: 1997
Original Price: $12
Market Value: $36

3   #86/101

New!

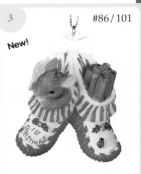

Bootie Baby (6th Edition)
Baby's First
Issued: 2000 • Current
Original Price: $11.50
Market Value: $11.50

4   #86/655

**Bundle Of Joy
(4th Edition)**
Baby's First
Issued: 1998 • Closed: 1998
Original Price: $12
Market Value: $20

5   #87/038

Bunny & Mouse Bell
Issued: 1993 • Retired: 1995
Original Price: $10.50
Market Value: N/E

6   #87/038

Bunny & Mouse Bell
Issued: 1993 • Retired: 1995
Original Price: $10.50
Market Value: N/E

7   #86/785

Catching ZZZ's
Issued: 1992 • Retired: 1995
Original Price: $12
Market Value: $47

DECK THE HALLS

	Price Paid	Value
1.		
2.		
3.		
4.		
5.		
6.		
7.		
Totals		

Ornaments

1 #86/710

Chauncey's First Christmas (2nd Edition)
Baby's First
Issued: 1997 • Closed: 1997
Original Price: $9
Market Value: $24

2 #86/787

Chickadees On Ball
Issued: 1992 • Retired: 1995
Original Price: $13.50
Market Value: N/E

3 #86/791

Chicks With Bead Garland
Issued: 1992 • Retired: 1995
Original Price: $17.50
Market Value: $215

4 #87/301

Christmas Cookies
Issued: 1995 • Retired: 1999
Original Price: $10
Market Value: $25

5 #87/301

Christmas Cookies
Issued: 1995 • Retired: 1999
Original Price: $10
Market Value: $25

6 #87/301

Christmas Cookies
Issued: 1995 • Retired: 1999
Original Price: $10
Market Value: $25

DECK THE HALLS

	Price Paid	Value
1.		
2.		
3.		
4.		
5.		
6.		
7.		
8.		
Totals		

7 #87/304

Christmas Flowers
Issued: 1995 • Current
Original Price: $12
Market Value: $13

8 #87/485

Christmas Stamps
Issued: 1996 • Retired: 1998
Original Price: $12
Market Value: $26

1 #86/796

A Cup Of Christmas Cheer
Issued: 1999 • Current
Original Price: $11.50
Market Value: $11.50

2 #86/784

The Drifters
Issued: 1992 • Retired: 1996
Original Price: $12
Market Value: $48

3 #86/784

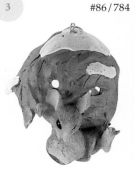

The Drifters
Issued: 1992 • Retired: 1996
Original Price: $12
Market Value: $48

4 #87/492

Fallen Angel
Issued: 1996 • Retired: 1998
Original Price: $12
Market Value: $26

5 #87/490

Flights Of Fancy
Issued: 1996 • Retired: 1998
Original Price: $12
Market Value: $26

6 #87/491

Frequent Flyer
Issued: 1996 • Retired: 1998
Original Price: $12
Market Value: $26

7 #86/789

Fresh Fruit
Issued: 1992 • Retired: 1995
Original Price: $12
Market Value: $42

8 #86/789

Fresh Fruit
Issued: 1992 • Retired: 1995
Original Price: $12
Market Value: $42

DECK THE HALLS

	Price Paid	Value
1.		
2.		
3.		
4.		
5.		
6.		
7.		
8.		
Totals		

Ornaments

1 #86/789

Fresh Fruit
Issued: 1992 • Retired: 1995
Original Price: $12
Market Value: $42

2 #87/971

Friends In Flight
Issued: 1994 • Retired: 1994
Original Price: $18
Market Value: $130

3 #87/186

The Grape Escape
Issued: 1994 • Retired: 1995
Original Price: $18
Market Value: $84

4 #87/186

The Grape Escape
Issued: 1994 • Retired: 1995
Original Price: $18
Market Value: $84

5 #87/941

Hang In There
Issued: 1993 • Retired: 1996
Original Price: $10
Market Value: $40

6 #87/941

Hang In There
Issued: 1993 • Retired: 1996
Original Price: $10
Market Value: $40

DECK THE HALLS

	Price Paid	Value
1.		
2.		
3.		
4.		
5.		
6.		
7.		
8.		

Totals

7 #87/941

Hang In There
Issued: 1993 • Retired: 1996
Original Price: $10
Market Value: $40

8 #86/656

Heading For The Slopes
Issued: 1998 • Current
Original Price: $13
Market Value: $13

1 #87/992

2 #86/102

New!

3 #87/299

High Flying Mackenzie
Issued: 1994 • Retired: 1997
Original Price: $20
Market Value: $55

Holiday Baking
Issued: 2000 • Current
Original Price: $11.50
Market Value: $11.50

Holiday Balloon Ride
Issued: 1995 • Retired: 1996
Original Price: $16
Market Value: $42

4 #87/969

5 #87/939

6 #87/939

Holiday Lights (lighted)
Issued: 1994 • Retired: 1995
Original Price: $10
Market Value: $50

Holiday Wreath
Issued: 1993 • Retired: 1995
Original Price: $12
Market Value: $50

Holiday Wreath
Issued: 1993 • Retired: 1995
Original Price: $12
Market Value: $50

7 #87/202

Horsing Around
Issued: 1994 • Retired: 1996
Original Price: $18
Market Value: $46

DECK THE HALLS

	Price Paid	Value
1.		
2.		
3.		
4.		
5.		
6.		
7.		
Totals		

Ornaments

1 #87/486

Letter To Santa
Issued: 1996 • Retired: 1998
Original Price: $12
Market Value: $30

2 #87/187

Mackenzie & Binkey Snacking
Issued: 1994 • Retired: 1994
Original Price: $12
Market Value: $70

3 #87/187

Mackenzie & Binkey Snacking
Issued: 1994 • Retired: 1994
Original Price: $12
Market Value: $70

4 #87/191

Mackenzie Blowing Bubbles
Issued: 1994 • Retired: 1994
Original Price: $12
Market Value: $68

5 #86/704

Mackenzie In Mitten
Issued: 1997 • Current
Original Price: $9
Market Value: $10.50

6 #87/940

Mackenzie Napping
Issued: 1993 • Retired: 1995
Original Price: $12
Market Value: $42

DECK THE HALLS

	Price Paid	Value
1.		
2.		
3.		
4.		
5.		
6.		
7.		
8.		

Totals

7 #87/970

Mackenzie On Ice
Issued: 1994 • Retired: 1996
Original Price: $10
Market Value: $46

8 #87/994

Mackenzie Snowball (Dated 1994)
Issued: 1994 • Closed: 1994
Original Price: $10
Market Value: $90

1   #87/192

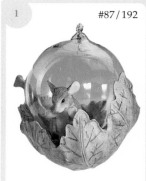

Mackenzie's Bubble Ride
Issued: 1994 • Retired: 1996
Original Price: $13
Market Value: $65

2   #86/709

Mackenzie's Jack-In-The-Box (Dated 1997)
Issued: 1997 • Closed: 1997
Original Price: $10
Market Value: $25

3   #87/300

Mackenzie's Whirligig
Issued: 1995 • Retired: 1997
Original Price: $20
Market Value: $42

4   #87/185

Maxine & Mackenzie
Issued: 1994 • Retired: 1996
Original Price: $12
Market Value: $38

5   #87/185

Maxine & Mackenzie
Issued: 1994 • Retired: 1996
Original Price: $12
Market Value: $38

6   #87/942

Maxine Lights A Candle (lighted)
Issued: 1993 • Retired: 1995
Original Price: $11
Market Value: $36

7   #86/701

Maxine's Angel
Issued: 1997 • Current
Original Price: $9
Market Value: $10.50

8   #86/788

Mice & Rabbit Ball
Issued: 1992 • Retired: 1995
Original Price: $12
Market Value: $78

DECK THE HALLS

	Price Paid	Value
1.		
2.		
3.		
4.		
5.		
6.		
7.		
8.		

Totals

Ornaments

1 #86/788

Mice & Rabbit Ball
Issued: 1992 • Retired: 1995
Original Price: $12
Market Value: $78

2 #86/786

Mice In A Leaf Sleigh
Issued: 1992 • Retired: 1995
Original Price: $26
Market Value: $245

3 #87/037

Mouse On Snowflake
Issued: 1993 • Retired: 1995
Original Price: $11
Market Value: $46

4 #87/045

**Mouse On Yellow Bulb
(lighted)**
Issued: 1994 • Retired: 1995
Original Price: $10
Market Value: $70

5 #87/532

**Our First Christmas 1996
(1st Edition)**
Issued: 1996 • Closed: 1996
Original Price: $18
Market Value: $44

6 #86/708

**Our First Christmas 1997
(2nd Edition)**
Issued: 1997 • Closed: 1997
Original Price: $12.50
Market Value: $25

Deck The Halls

	Price Paid	Value
1.		
2.		
3.		
4.		
5.		
6.		
7.		
8.		

Totals

7 #86/103

New!

**Our First Christmas
(5th Edition)**
Issued: 2000 • Current
Original Price: $11.50
Market Value: $11.50

8 #86/653

**Our First Christmas
Together (3rd Edition)**
Issued: 1998 • Closed: 1998
Original Price: $12
Market Value: $22

1 #86/798

Our First Christmas Together (4th Edition)
Issued: 1999 • Closed: 1999
Original Price: $11.50
Market Value: N/E

2 #86/2000

Peace On Earth (LE-1999)
Issued: 1999 • Closed: 1999
Original Price: $12
Market Value: $22

3 #87/027

Pear House (lighted)
Issued: 1994 • Retired: 1995
Original Price: $13
Market Value: $82

4 #87/314

Peppermint Party
Issued: 1995 • Retired: 1998
Original Price: $10
Market Value: $30

5 #87/314

Peppermint Party
Issued: 1995 • Retired: 1998
Original Price: $10
Market Value: $30

6 #86/659

Pine Cone Predicament (Dated 1998)
Issued: 1998 • Closed: 1998
Original Price: $11
Market Value: $20

7 #87/036

Porcelain Mouse Bell
Issued: 1993 • Retired: 1995
Original Price: $5
Market Value: $250

8 #87/302

Reginald In Leaves
Issued: 1995 • Retired: 1997
Original Price: $10
Market Value: $34

DECK THE HALLS

	Price Paid	Value
1.		
2.		
3.		
4.		
5.		
6.		
7.		
8.		
Totals		

1 #87 / 302

Reginald In Leaves
Issued: 1995 • Retired: 1997
Original Price: $10
Market Value: $34

2 #87 / 199

Reginald's Bubble Ride
Issued: 1994 • Retired: 1994
Original Price: $12
Market Value: $72

3 #86 / 657

Ski Jumper
Issued: 1998 • Current
Original Price: $13
Market Value: $13

4 #86 / 797

Snowbird 1999 Annual
(Dated 1999)
Issued: 1999 • Closed: 1999
Original Price: $11.50
Market Value: $18

5 #86 / 707

A Special Delivery
Issued: 1997 • Current
Original Price: $9
Market Value: $10

6 #87 / 483

Stamp Dispenser
Issued: 1996 • Current
Original Price: $12
Market Value: $13

7 #87 / 308

Stewart At Play
Issued: 1995 • Retired: 1995
Original Price: $12
Market Value: $42

DECK THE HALLS

	Price Paid	Value
1.		
2.		
3.		
4.		
5.		
6.		
7.		
Totals		

1   #87/307

Stewart's Winter Fun
Issued: 1995 • Retired: 1995
Original Price: $10
Market Value: $42

2   #87/307

Stewart's Winter Fun
Issued: 1995 • Retired: 1995
Original Price: $10
Market Value: $42

3   #87/991

Sticky Situations
Issued: 1994 • Retired: 1996
Original Price: $16
Market Value: $50

4   #87/991

Sticky Situations
Issued: 1994 • Retired: 1996
Original Price: $16
Market Value: $50

5   #86/104

New!

Teacher
Issued: 2000 • Current
Original Price: $11.50
Market Value: $11.50

6   #86/658

Tricycle Built From Treats
Issued: 1998 • Current
Original Price: $13
Market Value: $13

7   #86/105

New!

Weee . . . Three Kings!
Issued: 2000 • Current
Original Price: $11.50
Market Value: $11.50

8   #87/493

Wheeeeee!
Issued: 1996 • Retired: 1998
Original Price: $12
Market Value: $27

DECK THE HALLS

	Price Paid	Value
1.		
2.		
3.		
4.		
5.		
6.		
7.		
8.		

Totals

CHARMING TAILS® MISCELLANEOUS PIECES

Over the years, Dean Griff has designed accessories to complement the Charming Tails collection. Among these items are baskets, candle climbers, candleholders and votives, card holders, musicals, ornaments hangers, Teeny Tiny Tails, tree toppers, waterglobes and wreaths, all of which are organized alphabetically by category within this section.

1   #87/506

Mice On Vine Basket
Issued: 1994 • Retired: 1995
Original Price: $55
Market Value: $425

2   #87/529

Mouse On Basket
Issued: 1994 • Retired: 1995
Original Price: $50
Market Value: $400

3   #87/189

Mouse Candle Climber
Issued: 1994 • Retired: 1995
Original Price: $8
Market Value: $60

4   #89/317

Bunny With Carrot Candleholder
Issued: 1994 • Retired: 1995
Original Price: $12
Market Value: $135

5   #89/315

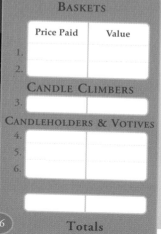

Duckling Votive
Issued: 1994 • Retired: 1994
Original Price: $12
Market Value: N/E

6   #85/400

Mouse Candleholder
Issued: 1993 • Retired: 1995
Original Price: $13
Market Value: $140

BASKETS	
Price Paid	Value
1.	
2.	
CANDLE CLIMBERS	
3.	
CANDLEHOLDERS & VOTIVES	
4.	
5.	
6.	
Totals	

Value Guide — CHARMING TAILS®

1 #85/400

Mouse Candleholder
Issued: 1993 • Retired: 1995
Original Price: $13
Market Value: $140

2 #87/502

Mouse In A Treehole Candleholder
Issued: 1994 • Retired: 1995
Original Price: $17
Market Value: $95

3 #87/503

Mouse On Leaf Candleholder
Issued: 1994 • Retired: 1995
Original Price: $17
Market Value: $120

4 #87/504

Mouse On Vine Candleholder
Issued: 1994 • Retired: 1995
Original Price: $55
Market Value: $500

5 #87/044

Mouse With Apple Candleholder
Issued: 1993 • Retired: 1995
Original Price: $13
Market Value: $115

6 #87/044

Mouse With Apple Candleholder
Issued: 1993 • Retired: 1995
Original Price: $13
Market Value: $115

7 #85/509

Pear Candleholder
Issued: 1994 • Retired: 1995
Original Price: $14
Market Value: $85

8 #85/510

Pumpkin Votive
Issued: 1994 • Retired: 1995
Original Price: $13.50
Market Value: $55

CANDLEHOLDERS & VOTIVES

	Price Paid	Value
1.		
2.		
3.		
4.		
5.		
6.		
7.		
8.		
Totals		

Miscellaneous Pieces

1   #87/509

Pyramid With Mice Candleholder
Issued: 1994 • Retired: 1995
Original Price: $40
Market Value: $475

2   #89/312

Rabbit/Daffodil Candleholder
Issued: 1994 • Retired: 1995
Original Price: $13.50
Market Value: $180

3   #89/312

Rabbit/Daffodil Candleholder
Issued: 1994 • Retired: 1995
Original Price: $13.50
Market Value: $180

4   #85/516

Stump Candleholder
Issued: 1994 • Retired: 1995
Original Price: $20
Market Value: $150

5   #85/516

Stump Candleholder
Issued: 1994 • Retired: 1995
Original Price: $20
Market Value: $150

6   #87/501

Mouse Card Holder
Issued: 1994 • Retired: 1995
Original Price: $13
Market Value: $47

CANDLEHOLDERS & VOTIVES

	Price Paid	Value
1.		
2.		
3.		
4.		
5.		

CARD HOLDERS

6.		

GENERAL MUSICALS

7.		
8.		

Totals

7   #86/790

Rocking Mice Musical
Issued: 1993 • Retired: 1994
Original Price: $65
Market Value: $400

8   #87/511

Skating Mouse Musical
Issued: 1994 • Retired: 1994
Original Price: $25
Market Value: $380

Value Guide — CHARMING TAILS®

1   #89/602

"Up, Up And Away"
Issued: 1995 • Retired: 1995
Original Price: $70
Market Value: $200

2   #889/681

The Berry Best Musical
Issued: 1997 • Closed: 1997
Original Price: $34.95
Market Value: N/E

3   #889/619

Bunny Buddies Musical
Issued: 1997 • Closed: 1997
Original Price: $34.95
Market Value: N/E

4   #889/682

**Catchin' Butterflies
Musical**
Issued: 1997 • Closed: 1997
Original Price: $34.95
Market Value: N/E

5   #889/623

Hangin' Around Musical
Issued: 1997 • Closed: 1997
Original Price: $34.95
Market Value: N/E

6   #889/617

Midday Snooze Musical
Issued: 1997 • Closed: 1997
Original Price: $34.95
Market Value: N/E

7   #889/683

**Reach For The
Stars Musical**
·Issued: 1996 • Closed: 1996
Original Price: $34.95
Market Value: N/E

GENERAL MUSICALS

	Price Paid	Value
1.		

SAN FRANCISCO MUSIC BOX MUSICALS

2.		
3.		
4.		
5.		
6.		
7.		
Totals		

Miscellaneous Pieces

1 #889/685

Spring Flowers Musical
Issued: 1996 • Closed: 1996
Original Price: $34.95
Market Value: N/E

2 #889/684

Thanks For Being There Musical
Issued: 1996 • Closed: 1996
Original Price: $34.95
Market Value: N/E

3 #889/680

The Waterslide Musical
Issued: 1997 • Closed: 1997
Original Price: $39.95
Market Value: N/E

4 #87/519

Leaf Vine Ornament Hanger
Issued: 1994 • Retired: 1995
Original Price: $25
Market Value: $66

5 #80/7

The Berry Toss Game
Issued: 1998 • Retired: 1999
Original Price: $14
Market Value: N/E

6 #80/10

The Big Winner
Issued: 1998 • Retired: 1999
Original Price: $12
Market Value: N/E

7 #80/4

The Daffodil Twirl (musical)
Issued: 1998 • Retired: 1999
Original Price: $49.50
Market Value: N/E

8 #80/3

Get Your Candy Apple Here!
Issued: 1998 • Retired: 1999
Original Price: $12
Market Value: N/E

SAN FRANCISCO MUSIC BOX MUSICALS

	Price Paid	Value
1.		
2.		
3.		

ORNAMENT HANGERS
4.		

TEENY TINY TAILS
5.		
6.		
7.		
8.		

Totals

Value Guide — CHARMING TAILS®

1   #80/6

Mushroom Carousel (musical)
Issued: 1998 • Retired: 1999
Original Price: $49.50
Market Value: N/E

2   #80/1

Off To The Fair
Issued: 1998 • Retired: 1999
Original Price: $15
Market Value: N/E

3   #80/5

Test Your Strength
Issued: 1998 • Retired: 1999
Original Price: $14
Market Value: N/E

4   #80/2

The Ticket Booth
Issued: 1998 • Retired: 1999
Original Price: $15
Market Value: N/E

5   #80/8

Tulip Ferris Wheel (musical)
Issued: 1998 • Retired: 1999
Original Price: $49.50
Market Value: N/E

6   #87/958

Mouse Star Treetop
Issued: 1993 • Retired: 1995
Original Price: $14
Market Value: $65

7   #87/476

All Snug In Their Beds
Issued: 1996 • Retired: 1996
Original Price: $30
Market Value: $63

8   #87/475

Baby's First Christmas Waterglobe
Issued: 1996 • Retired: 1996
Original Price: $28
Market Value: $70

TEENY TINY TAILS

	Price Paid	Value
1.	20.00	37.50
2.	5.00	15.00
3.		
4.		
5.		

TREE TOPPERS

6.

WATERGLOBES

7.
8.

Totals   91

1 — #87/542

Jawbreakers
Issued: 1994 • Retired: 1995
Original Price: $40
Market Value: $100

2 — #87/518

Letter To Santa Waterglobe
Issued: 1994 • Retired: 1994
Original Price: $45
Market Value: $122

3 — #89/555

Me Next
Issued: 1995 • Retired: 1995
Original Price: $45
Market Value: $215

4 — #87/956

Mini Surprise
Issued: 1994 • Retired: 1994
Original Price: $22
Market Value: $80

5 — #92/224

Mouse On Cheese
Issued: 1994 • Retired: 1995
Original Price: $44
Market Value: N/E

6 — #92/225

Mouse On Rubber Duck
Issued: 1994 • Retired: 1995
Original Price: $44
Market Value: $135

7 — #89/557

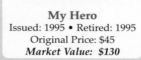

My Hero
Issued: 1995 • Retired: 1995
Original Price: $45
Market Value: $130

8 — #85/778

Pumpkin Playtime Waterglobe
Issued: 1995 • Retired: 1995
Original Price: $35
Market Value: $120

WATERGLOBES

	Price Paid	Value
1.		
2.		
3.		
4.		
5.		
6.		
7.		
8.		
Totals		

Value Guide — CHARMING TAILS®

1 #87/200

Sailing Away Waterglobe
Issued: 1994 • Retired: 1994
Original Price: $50
Market Value: $250

2 #87/517

Sharing The Warmth
Issued: 1994 • Retired: 1994
Original Price: $40
Market Value: $125

3 #87/534

Sweet Dreams
Issued: 1994 • Retired: 1994
Original Price: $40
Market Value: $280

4 #87/530

Together At Christmas
Issued: 1994 • Retired: 1995
Original Price: $30
Market Value: $86

5 #87/516

Trimmings For The Tree
Issued: 1994 • Retired: 1994
Original Price: $45
Market Value: $140

6 #89/556

Underwater Explorer
Issued: 1995 • Retired: 1995
Original Price: $45
Market Value: $150

7 #87/505

Mouse On Vine Wreath
Issued: 1994 • Retired: 1995
Original Price: $55
Market Value: $430

WATERGLOBES		
	Price Paid	Value
1.		
2.		
3.		
4.		
5.		
6.		
WREATHS		
7.		
Totals		

93

LEAF & ACORN CLUB® PIECES

Now in its third year of existence, Fitz and Floyd's *The Leaf & Acorn Club* is better than ever! Members will have the chance to obtain three new membership pieces (in addition to the members only piece) in the year 2000, which will bring the total number of exclusive club pieces to 13.

#97/17

And The Stars!
Issued: 1999 • Closed: 1999
Original Price: N/A
Market Value: N/E

#97/12

**A Growing Friendship
(Members Only Piece)**
Issued: 1998 • Closed: 1998
Original Price: $17
Market Value: $50

#97/10

**Leaf & Acorn Club
Lapel Pin (Charter
Membership Piece)**
Issued: 1997 • Closed: 1998
Original Price: N/A
Market Value: $20

#98/701

**Maxine's Leaf Collection
(Members Only Piece)**
Issued: 1997 • Closed: 1998
Original Price: $15
Market Value: $40

#97/14

**Nap Time Lapel Pin
(Membership Piece)**
Issued: 1999 • Closed: 1999
Original Price: N/A
Market Value: $12

#97/21

New!

**Peek-A-Boo Bouquet
(Members Only Piece)**
Issued: 2000 • Current
Original Price: $22
Market Value: $22

LEAF & ACORN
CLUB PIECES

	Price Paid	Value
1.		
2.		
3.		
4.		
5.		
6.		

Totals

1   #97/15

Ring Around The Rosie
(Members Only Piece)
Issued: 1999 • Closed: 1999
Original Price: $23
Market Value: $26

2   #97/13

Sharing A Warm And Cozy Holiday (Members Only Piece)
Issued: 1998 • Closed: 1998
Original Price: $23
Market Value: $45

3   #97/16

A Snowy Trio
(Members Only Piece)
Issued: 1999 • Closed: 1999
Original Price: $21
Market Value: $38

4   #98/700

Thank You
(Charter Membership Piece)
Issued: 1997 • Closed: 1998
Original Price: N/A
Market Value: $36

5   #97/20

New!

This Is The Key Lapel Pin
(Membership Piece)
Issued: 2000 • Current
Original Price: N/A
Market Value: N/E

6   #97/11

You Are My Shining Star
(Membership Piece)
Issued: 1999 • Closed: 1999
Original Price: N/A
Market Value: $24

7   #97/18

New!

You Hold The Key To My Heart
(Membership Piece)
Issued: 2000 • Current
Original Price: N/A
Market Value: N/E

LEAF & ACORN CLUB PIECES		
	Price Paid	Value
1.		
2.		
3.		
4.		
5.		
6.		
7.		
Totals		

 Future Releases

Use this page to record future releases and purchases.

Charming Tails	Item #	Status	Price Paid	Market Value

Page Total:	Price Paid	Value

🌰 Future Releases 🌰

Use this page to record future releases and purchases.

Charming Tails	Item #	Status	Price Paid	Market Value

Page Total:	Price Paid	Value

Total Value Of My Collection

Record the Page Totals from the Value Guide section here.

Figurines		
Page Number	Price Paid	Market Value
Page 29		
Page 30		
Page 31		
Page 32		
Page 33		
Page 34		
Page 35		
Page 36		
Page 37		
Page 38		
Page 39		
Page 40		
Page 41		
Page 42		
Page 43		
Page 44		
Page 45		
Page 46		
Subtotal		

Figurines, cont.		
Page Number	Price Paid	Market Value
Page 46		
Page 47		
Page 48		
Page 49		
Page 50		
Page 51		
Page 52		
Page 53		
Page 54		
Page 55		
Page 56		
Page 57		
Page 58		
Page 59		
Page 60		
Page 61		
Page 62		
Page 63		
Subtotal		

Grand Total:	Price Paid	Value

Total Value Of My Collection

Record the Page Totals from the Value Guide section here.

Figurines, cont.

Page Number	Price Paid	Market Value
Page 64		
Page 65		
Page 66		
Page 67		
Page 68		
Page 69		
Page 70		

Ornaments

Page Number	Price Paid	Market Value
Page 71		
Page 72		
Page 73		
Page 74		
Page 75		
Page 76		
Page 77		
Page 78		
Page 79		
Page 80		
Subtotal		

Ornaments, cont.

Page Number	Price Paid	Market Value
Page 81		
Page 82		
Page 83		
Page 84		
Page 85		

Miscellaneous

Page 86		
Page 87		
Page 88		
Page 89		
Page 90		
Page 91		
Page 92		
Page 93		

The Leaf & Acorn Club

Page 94		
Page 95		
Subtotal		

Grand Total:	Price Paid	Value

SECONDARY MARKET OVERVIEW

*T*f you're looking to acquire some new neighbors for your friends in Squashville, you may discover that some pieces are harder to find than others. The adorable woodland critters of Charming Tails are among the most elusive animals in the wild world of collectibles, so you might not find all of them by prowling around their natural habitat at your favorite collectibles store. Some of them have moved on to the next pasture, better known to collectors as the secondary market! It is here that you'll be able to network with other collectors, share information about your collection, and find that "gotta-have-it" piece to add to your shelf.

A SECONDARY WHAT?

Charming Tails are generally retired twice a year, making way for a whole new batch of charming critters. When that happens, the mold for each retired piece is broken so that it can never be made again. Naturally, this shuts off the supply of that piece to retailers and collectors must look elsewhere to find the product. Once the demand outweighs supply of the piece, the value of that piece also tends to increase and a secondary market is formed.

However, retirement is not the only method which can increase a piece's value on the secondary market. Suspended pieces also experience an increase in value when they are removed from production. Suspended pieces differ from retirements in that they are removed from production, but their molds are not broken as they may be reintroduced within the line at a later time.

Limited edition pieces, just as the name implies, are only produced in limited quantities. These pieces can be limited by either production number or length of time. For example, "Binkey's Bouncing Bundle" is a limited edition of 7,500, so only 7,500 figurines were made before the mold was broken. "Steady Wins The Race" was an limited edition for 1998, which means that its production was stopped at the end of the year, at which time the mold was broken. As limited editions are produced in smaller quantities, their value is often higher than that of other pieces on the secondary market.

Similar to limited edition figurines are exclusive pieces. Exclusive pieces are only available at special events or through selected stores or catalogs. Members of *The Leaf & Acorn Club* are entitled to certain exclusive figurines as a privilege of membership. Keep in mind that exclusive pieces also usually carry a higher price tag on the secondary market.

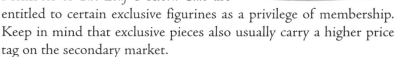

When the Charming Tails line first made its debut, it was not intended to be a collectible line. Most of the pieces were functional items like candleholders or ornaments. But since the figurines have become a hot collectible item, fans of Charming Tails have started to view these pieces as "collectors items" and their value has risen accordingly.

Pieces which have been signed by artist Dean Griff also tend to be more coveted, and worth more on the secondary market, than their unsigned counterparts. Each year since 1995, Fitz and Floyd has been sponsoring events at collectibles stores where devoted collectors can buy special figurines and have them signed by the artist.

So now that you know some of the types of pieces that are available in the collection, it might help to know where you can find the secondary market to get your hands on them.

READY, SET, SHOP!

If you have access to the Internet, finding a Charming Tails piece can be as simple as clicking a mouse (not Mackenzie or Maxine, but the one attached to your computer!). In cyberspace, you will find a plethora of retailers message boards, and sites set up by other collectors devoted to those darling animals of Squashville! Auction sites can help you locate a number of pieces for sale. Even if you're not looking for the secondary market, the Internet can also be a wonderful place to form lasting friendships with other people who share your passion for collecting Dean Griff's Charming Tails!

Another place to begin your hunt might be right under your nose – your local retail store! Even if your local retailer doesn't carry the retired piece you want, the dealer may know of other collectors close by who are interested in buying, selling or trading pieces. Retail stores also may occasionally host secondary market shows for their regular customers.

The classified ads in your local paper might be another helpful resource. Newspapers often have an "Antiques/Collectibles" section where you might find someone looking to exchange pieces with other collectors. But newspapers don't cater to collectors alone, so you may not want to use your local paper as your only method of accessing the secondary market.

Secondary market exchange services provide collectors with a regularly published list of items for sale in exchange for a subscription fee. Keep in mind, however, that these organizations also usually charge a commission on every sale they broker.

When you finally find the piece you want, remember that several factors can affect its value. It's one thing to buy an ornament or figurine from a store, where it has come directly from the factory. But buying one from the secondary market is something else entirely! Know your seller. Get references from previous buyers and be always sure to check the seller's feedback if you are making a transaction through an auction site. If possible, take a good look at the piece you are about to buy, or request to see pictures of it if you're using the Internet.

CONDITION & QUALITY

Some of the Charming Tails figurines available on the secondary market may have been damaged and repaired. They could also contain slight flaws that occurred during production, like stray wisps of paint. Pieces which have been chipped, damaged or have suffered "factory flaws" should be listed as so. It is perfectly legitimate to buy restored or slightly damaged pieces, but you shouldn't pay full secondary market value for them. Another factor which has a large impact on value is packaging. Many collectors won't even consider buying a Charming Tails figurine unless it comes in its original box, though many will . . . just at lower than secondary market value.

The most important thing to remember is that collecting Charming Tails is supposed to be fun. So when you're surfing the Internet or scanning the classifieds to find that all-important piece, enjoy yourself! For most people, the quest is just as much fun as the end result!

SECONDARY MARKET SPEAK

damaged box (DB) – a secondary market term used when a collectible's box is in poor condition, often times diminishing the value of the item.

mint in box (MIB) – a secondary market term used when a collectible's original box is "good as new," which usually adds to the value of the item.

no box (NB) – a secondary market term used when a collectible's original box is missing. For most collectibles, having the original box is a factor in the value.

Dealers, Exchanges And Resources

Best Collectibles
P.O. Box 152
Morganton, GA 30560
(706) 838-5920
www.bestcollectibles.com

Donna's Collectibles Exchange
703 Endeavor Drive South
Winter Springs, FL 32708
(800) 480-5105
www.donnascollexch.com

Elaine's Mouse Trap
850 Grace Street
Herndon, VA 20170
(703) 478-9315
fax: (703) 478-9316
home.earthlink.net/~elainep
elainesmousetrap@aol.com

www.charmingdave.com.

Jan & Cat's Charming Tails Forum
Cathy Hauk
1725 East Sycamore St.
Canton, IL 61520
(309) 647-5805
http://bearsnbuddies.com/ctails/home.htm

Michelle's Charming Tails Resource
c/o Michelle Benoit Walker
610 Church Street
Thibodaux, LA 70301

New England Collectibles Exchange
Bob Dorman
201 Pine Avenue
Clarksburg, MA 01247
(413) 663-3643
nece@collectiblesbroker.com
www.collectiblesbroker.com

Warren Rogers
211 Back Road
Windham, CT 06280
(860) 456-7090
wrogers01@snet.net

INSURING YOUR COLLECTION

Now that you've devoted a lot of time, effort and money to building up your Charming Tails collection, make sure that your collection is covered in the event of theft, flood, fire or other unforeseen circumstances. Insuring your collection is a wise move, and it doesn't have to be costly or difficult.

1. Assess the value of your Charming Tails collection. If your collection is quite extensive, you might want to have it professionally appraised. However, you can determine the current value of your collection yourself by consulting a reputable price guide such as the Collector's Value Guide™.

2. Determine the amount of coverage you need. Collectibles are often covered under a basic homeowner's or renter's policy, but ask your agent if your policy covers fire, theft, flood, hurricanes, earthquakes and damage or breakage from routine handling. Also, find out if your policy covers claims at "current replacement value" — the amount it would cost to replace items if they were damaged, lost or stolen. If the amount of insurance does not cover your collection, you may want to consider adding a Personal Articles Floater or a Fine Arts Floater ("rider") to your policy. Many insurance companies specialize in collectibles insurance and can help you ensure that your collection is adequately covered.

3. Keep up-to-date documentation of your collectible pieces and their values. Save all your receipts and photograph each item, taking special care to show variations, artist signatures and other special features in the photograph. Keep your documentation in a safe place, such as a safe deposit box, or make two copies and give one to a friend or relative.

VARIATIONS

*F*or the past decade, the Charming Tails line has been evolving and growing through the creative talent and vision of Dean Griff. Produced first by Silvestri and then by Fitz and Floyd, the line has been subjected to the highest standards of quality in the production and assembly process. Occasionally, however, variations in design may occur as the result of either deliberate changes in production or human error, since each piece is assembled and painted by hand. Common variations within the Charming Tails collection include changes in name, color and design.

PALE MICE

One of the most common differences within the collection is a consistent color difference in the mice, especially in the earliest pieces. Over 20 figurines and ornaments with the paler, tan and pink mice were issued between 1993 and 1994, including the 1993 releases, "Gourd Slide" and "Acorn Built For Two." While some collectors may be attracted to the more realistic, darker brown mouse design used in later pieces, others intentionally seek out the older pieces with the lighter colored mice simply because they wish to own the earliest pieces released in the Charming Tails collection. Significant changes in secondary market value can be attributed to the fact that these are early pieces and not necessarily because they feature the "pale mice."

DESIGN CHANGES

Differences in design can occur for several reasons. Often, a variation in design attributed to human error in the factory only occurs on a few pieces. These differences are usually slight, and may consist of part of the piece being misplaced or completely left off of the piece. A second source of design changes are decisions made by the manufacturer to alter the design during the timespan in which the piece is produced. One example of a design change is "Keeping Our Love Alive," in which some versions have holly leaves and berries decorating the flower pot while others do not. Another example is "Stewart's Choo-Choo Ride," in which the ribbon on the top of Stewart's railroad car can be found on both the front and the rear end of the roof. Additionally, the white area around Stewart's eyes and the number of holly berries on the side of the car varies.

It is important to remember that sometimes modifications are made after the initial sample, or prototype, is reviewed, yet the revised piece is not finalized in time for its photograph to be included in the current catalog. In this case, a discrepancy is found between the piece pictured in the Charming Tails catalog and the actual figurine purchased at your retailer. (For more information, see our sidebar on "Artist Proofs.")

ARTIST PROOFS

Occasionally, a collector will stumble across a piece which is not recognized in the Charming Tails catalogs. This piece may be an "artist proof," a prototype of a design which has been used to experiment with different colors, patterns and/or design elements before the piece is released. While most of these designs are eventually produced, the design often differs from the initial version, thus causing them to carry an often hefty price tag on the secondary market. One example of an existing prototype is the 1997 *Leaf & Acorn Club* Charter Membership Piece "Thank You." While the version which was released features Mackenzie with an ink bottle, an artist proof shows Chauncey standing amongst colored papers with "Thanks" written on each.

Names of pieces can also be changed during the production process, the most famous example of this being the limited edition piece "Fragile – Handle With Care" (LE-15,000). The first shipment, or approximately 1,000 of these figurines, was incorrectly stamped with the name "Love Doesn't Come With Instructions." When this was brought to the attention of Fitz and Floyd, new figurines were then stamped with the original name, "Fragile – Handle With Care." However, during the production of the figurine's final 1,608 pieces, the limited edition information was omitted from the bottomstamp of the piece. Two different production marks, an acorn and a maple leaf, can also be found on the bottoms of these figurines, which were produced over a two year period.

While most variations that are found can add interest and intrigue to a Charming Tails collection, only sometimes will they command a higher value on the secondary market. One exception is the activity found surrounding the figurine, "Fragile – Handle With Care." To date, a substantial increase of $80 represents the value of the incorrectly stamped pieces over those stamped with the correct name.

Whether or not some of the other variations will soon see a similar rise to that of "Fragile – Handle With Care," remains to be seen. However, through the history of Fitz and Floyd's Charming Tails, variations have proved to be an area of interest for many collectors. So, if you're looking to expand your collection, often times finding that special piece may mean finding one like no other!

Club News

*T*f you can't get enough of Mackenzie, Binkey and their fellow citizens of Squashville, you're not alone. There are plenty of other collectors out there . . . enough to have made *The Leaf & Acorn Club* one of the hottest collector's clubs in the industry.

Introduced in 1997, *The Leaf & Acorn Club* is the official collector's club for Charming Tails. As the club now enters its third year of membership, it has grown to become a nationwide family of like-minded people who share a fondness for Mackenzie Mouse and his his pals.

For an application fee of only $29.50, collectors who join the club in 2000 will receive plenty of special benefits that are unavailable to non-members. Just for joining, you'll receive the Membership Figurine "You Hold The Key To My Heart," which features Mackenzie unlocking the door to a world of hopes and dreams for the new century. In addition, you'll receive the 2000 Charming Tails lapel pin, "This Is The Key." That key is your entry into a whimsical world of joy and happiness for you to share with Charming Tails fans just like you! This darling lapel pin is also a great way for you and your fellow club members to recognize each other!

As a club member, you are not obligated to buy anything else. But only members can take advantage of the two special Members Only exclusive figurines which are offered by *The Leaf & Acorn Club* each year. "Peek-A-Boo Bouquet" serves as the first Members Only piece for 2000. You won't be able to resist these happy critters as they play a friendly game of hide-and-seek! An order form for this adorable piece is included in your club packet.

Members of *The Leaf & Acorn Club* can keep up with the lives and times of Mackenzie, Maxine and all their friends with a subscription to the *Squashville Gazette*, the club's official newsletter. With all the latest information about new releases, retirements and Squashville gossip within its pages, this newsletter will help you to be the ultimate Charming Tails insider! A one-year subscription to the Squashville Gazette is your complimentary gift for joining *The Leaf & Acorn Club*. In addition, you'll receive the latest Charming Tails catalog, filled with pictures of every current and retired piece in the Charming Tails line.

Finally, your club membership card is your ticket to some of the greatest special events in Charming Tails history – events so special that they're kept secret! Fitz and Floyd might surprise you with an invitation to an appearance by the talented Dean Griff, where you may even get him to sign your favorite piece!

To become part of the Charming Tails family, you can use the application in the back of this book. You can also get an application from your local authorized retailer. To receive an application in the mail, you can contact *The Leaf & Acorn Club* directly at:

> THE LEAF & ACORN CLUB
> P.O. Box 972124
> Dallas, TX 75397-2124
> (877) 435-CLUB
>
> or visit the Charming Tails web site at
> **www.charmingtails.com**

Honeybourne Hollow™

*D*ean Griff's whimsical mice, bunnies and raccoons aren't the only wild animals to emerge out of the Fitz and Floyd wilderness. A much larger woodland beast has made its debut from Fitz and Floyd, and it's an animal found often in the collectibles world. That's right – it's a bear!

A creation of artist Pat Sebern, The Bears of Honeybourne Hollow made its debut at the International Collectibles Exposition in Rosemont in June of 1999. Since then, the irresistible bears have been drawing attention from retailers and collectors across the country.

According to the legend, the village of Honeybourne Hollow came about as the result of one little girl's wish upon a star. This little girl, whose name is Patty, fell in love with the two marble bear statues that were perched out-side the town's library. She named the bears Byron and Briggs, and grew so affectionate towards them that she wished they would come to life, even though she knew it would mean losing them. After all, bears belong in the wild, not on a pedestal! Before Patty went to sleep one night, she wished upon a twinkling star that Byron and Briggs could live in the wilderness.

The next morning, Byron found himself out in the middle of the woods and very much alive! He quickly set out to find the perfect

habitat, a "bear paradise" where all bruins could live together in harmony. He found that place in a wooded area known as Honeybourne. A true pioneer, Byron set about building a village for himself, and it wasn't long before Emma and her cubs Blossom and Burke happened upon the scene and offered to run the town bakery. Now the colony has grown into an "official" town with Byron act-ing as the elected mayor and a population of almost 20 bears, with more sure to follow.

Fifteen figurines have gotten this line off to a great start, all of them featuring the villager bears of Honeybourne Hollow. They'll

do anything for fun, like painting a little house for the local birds in "Building Memories," learning that "Sharing Warms The Heart" by rustling up a batch of cookies or sharing a scarf with a cold snowbear in "Friendship Keeps Us Warm."

By the way, if you look closely, you'll notice that all of these adorable bears wear slippers! Ever since Byron stepped on a bee while building the bakery, the

bears have been extra careful to protect their paws! So now every piece features a bear with slippers – except one. The limited edition piece "Follow Your Dreams" shows the brave Byron before his traumatic stinging experience, while he was still in search of a place to settle down in the woods.

With these bears on the scene, Fitz and Floyd is sure to have created another winner in the collectibles world. And since the line has just gotten started, collectors are left with a lot of irresistibly unan-

swered questions. What happened to Byron's good buddy Briggs? Who'll be stopping by Honeybourne Hollow next? What will the future bring for this delightful community of bruins? To find out where the story leads, you'll just have to wait for the next chapter in this tiny tale of a bear's town!

PRODUCTION, PACKAGING AND PRICING

*T*he Charming Tails characters have brought the joy of the great outdoors into the homes of collectors since 1992. The journey from Squashville to your home begins once artist Dean Griff has finalized his design, and takes pieces as far as Asia, where the resin collectibles are manufactured.

Charming Tails pieces arrive on store shelves wrapped in bubble wrap or styrofoam to protect them from the hazards of shipping and are contained in a white box accented with a green stripe, which is quite different from the plain brown boxes the pieces originally came in! Newer boxes can be found in two versions: one with a leaf pattern and the other with the logo stripe drawn in the design of a ribbon. Most boxes also feature the Charming Tails logo and a picture of the piece. The piece itself is often accompanied with a cardboard name tag, which can be displayed along with the piece.

Beginning in 1996, production marks found their way onto the bottom of Charming Tails pieces as a way to identify which year the piece was produced. The symbol for 1996 was an acorn, 1997, a maple leaf, 1998, a pawprint, 1999, a pumpkin and 2000, a bird. Along with the production mark, the piece's name and stock number, logo and company trademark also appear. Pieces produced before 1996 may have a wealth of different information, from company stickers and stamps, to no information whatsoever.

Adding new figurines to your collection usually runs from $10 to $20, but pieces with several characters may be priced higher. Ornaments are also in the $10 to $20 range, while waterglobes are more expensive, costing between $28 and $50. Whatever your budget, there is sure to be a Charming Tails piece that fits the bill!

CARING FOR YOUR COLLECTION

*C*hauncey Chipmunk, Stewart Skunk and Mackenzie Mouse might spend their free time romping through Squashville with reckless abandon, but your figurines and ornaments need to be cared for if you want to preserve their beauty and value.

Many Charming Tails pieces are seasonal, so you probably won't be displaying "Mackenzie Claus On Parade" during the summer or "Binkey's Bouncing Bundle" in the winter. If you choose to store your figurines away during this time, repack them in the original boxes and packing foam they came in. This should protect your figurines as securely as the day they were purchased from the store.

Dust is probably the worst adversary faced by your Charming Tails. An occasional light dusting with a soft brush is all that is necessary. Don't dust your collection roughly. Figurines are made of resin and can be delicate (and Mackenzie and Maxine prefer to be handled gently!). Although your figurines may like nothing better than spending "A Day At The Lake," don't try washing them if they get dirty. Water can ruin your figurines. Harsh cleaners should also be avoided.

The lighted buildings that make up Squashville Village need only infrequent care. If you don't plan on lighting your village pieces for a while, remove the batteries from them. Nothing will ruin your village faster than old, leaking batteries. Keeping your village unlit for short periods of time when you are not admiring it may extend the life of the bulbs and prevent them from burning out quickly. The citizens of Squashville would not like it if the "Cantaloupe Cathedral" or "Great Oak Town Hall" were to go dark.

Keeping these simple care tips in mind should keep your collection in tip-top shape for years to come.

CHARMING TAILS® ON DISPLAY

*W*hile display cabinets are always an option, there are also many other creative ways to show off your Charming Tails collection. With just a little time and effort you can bring your woodland creatures to life through creative environments which are sure to catch the attention of guests. Most importantly, use your imagination and don't be afraid to try new things! Here are some ideas to help get you started.

IN THE GARDEN

Since mice, rabbits, squirrels and chipmunks are most at home in "the great outdoors," try showcasing your critters in their natural habitat! Set up a miniature flower, herb or vegetable garden near a window that receives plenty of sunlight and  decorate with some garden-themed Charming Tails. For instance, "After Lunch Snooze" and "Tuggin' Twosome" show characters both at work and at rest among the vegetables, while "Binkie In A Bed Of Flowers" and "Hangin' Around" look adorable tucked into a bed of flowers. (Helpful hint: place plastic wrap or green cloth under your figurines to avoid contact with the soil and to keep them clean.)

SPICE UP YOUR KITCHEN

 Here is another idea to incorporate some more "unexpected" items into your display. Try hiding themed pieces such as "Stewart's Apple Costume" or "Harvest Fruit" among the rest of your fruit in a decorative basket and see who is the first to notice! Or sweeten up a tray of baked

goods by adding pieces such as "Pumpkin Pie," and "How Many Candles?" You'll be surprised how many of your guests grab for these delicious looking treats!

ACCENT WITH ACCESSORIES

A single figurine standing alone can often have a powerful effect on a room. Use pieces such as "Even The Ups And Downs Are Fun" in the children's playroom or "Feeding Time" in the dining room to give a whimsical and fun look to a traditionally decorated room.

A LASTING KEEPSAKE

Use your collection to help commemorate a special event in your life. To keep the memory of your wedding day, for example, fresh in your mind, drape some white material over a table or shelf and decorate with the bulletin from the service, dried flowers and champagne glasses. Adorn with pieces from "The Wedding" for a lasting tribute to your love.

BASKETS

Baskets are perfect homes for your favorite Charming Tails pieces. Purchase a medium-sized decorative basket or use a Charming Tails custom-designed basket and fill it with wood shavings or artificial grass. Place an assortment of packaged tea bags, coffees, crackers and cookies in the basket. And don't forget to add an appropriate Charming Tails piece or two. Try "Fragile – Handle With Care" or "You

Couldn't Be Sweeter." You can place your basket on the kitchen counter or in the dining room or you can share your love of Charming Tails with a friend by giving the basket as a birthday surprise or get-well sentiment!

A Tail For All Seasons

Since many of the Charming Tails pieces are designed with a seasonal theme, they lend themselves towards displays which use outdoor accents. These sorts of displays are great because they bring the wonder of nature into your home.

Spring: Scatter some artificial grass and arrange your spring and Easter themed Charming Tails to look as though they are participating in various outdoor activities. "Chickie Back Ride" and "Chickie Chariot Ride" can run races all day among miniature potted plants and Easter accessories dispersed throughout the scene.

Summer: As the warm weather rolls around, treat your Charming Tails to "A Day At The Lake." Blue painted plexiglass or cardboard wrapped with blue paper can serve as a pond for the characters, who can spend the day "Gone Fishin'" and enjoying a "Rowboat Romance." But remember: Avoid using real water in your displays, as it can ruin your Charming Tails figurines.

Autumn: As the leaves turn color, your Charming Tails are ready to celebrate! Scatter dried leaves over a red or orange cloth and decorate with chestnuts and twigs. Arrange several figurines in the background to look as though they are working and playing together. "Autumn Harvest" pieces work especially well in this display.

Winter: Cover a white cloth with "snow" made of cotton to resemble a wintry day. Purchase train tracks from a local craft shop, and set the Charming Choo-Choo cars on top. Surround the tracks

with animals playing and frolicking in the snow or on a frozen lake. Lightly sprinkle the display with plastic "snow" for a touch of realism.

Don't overlook craft stores when thinking up displays! Craft and hobby shops often contain nearly everything you need to create a wide variety of displays, from snowcapped trees to silk flowers to miniature

accessories for your figurines. These shops are also great for sparking the imagination to come up with brand new display ideas!

No matter what kind of display you choose, don't forget that the main objective is to have fun!

SQUASHVILLE COMES ALIVE!

Don't forget the Squashville Village pieces when setting up a Charming Tails display. These buildings and accessories, many of which are lighted, give the environment a comfortable, homey feel.

GLOSSARY

accessory – a piece designed to enhance the display of Charming Tails figurines.

assorted – pieces which share the same stock number, but can be purchased separately.

closed – a piece whose production was limited by either time or quantity and is no longer available from the manufacturer.

current – any piece which is in production and available in retail stores.

exclusive – a figurine made especially for, and only available through, a specific store, exposition or buying group.

"Griffware" – giftware pieces designed by Dean Griff prior to Charming Tails.

issue price – the retail price of an item when it was introduced.

limited edition (LE) – a piece scheduled for a predetermined production quantity or time. Some pieces have been limited to a specific number or limited by year of production.

open – a Charming Tails piece which is currently in production and available in stores.

production mark – also called a "year mark." Used by Charming Tails since 1996, a production mark is a symbol found on the bottom of a piece that indicates the year the piece was produced.

resin – a liquid used to bind together various materials, such as wood, shells or porcelain, for the production of a Charming Tails collectible.

retired – a piece which is taken out of production, never to be made again, usually followed by a scarcity of the piece and a rise in value on the secondary market.

event piece – a figurine which was released for a specific happening, such as a collectibles convention or a retail event.

suspended – a piece that has been removed from production by Fitz and Floyd but may return in the future, possibly with slight design modifications.

variations – pieces that have color, design or printed text changes from the "original" piece. Some of these changes are minor, while some are important enough to affect the value of a piece on the secondary market.

ALPHABETICAL INDEX

– Key –

All Charming Tails pieces are listed below in alphabetical order. The first number refers to the piece's location within the Value Guide section and the second to the box in which it is pictured on that page.

Alphabetical Index

ACKNOWLEDGEMENTS

Checkerbee Publishing would like to extend special thanks to Suzanne Gamble, Max and Linda Hughes, Phyllis Lester, Dave Reid, Warren Rogers and all the great people at Fitz and Floyd.

As we begin a new Millennium, The Leaf & Acorn Club enters its third year. Make sure you are a part of the Charming Tails Family by joining the Club. As a member you will enjoy many exclusive benefits.

CLUB MEMBERSHIP PIECES

As a 2000 Leaf & Acorn Club Member you will receive "You Hold The Key To My Heart," . . . just for joining the Club! Designed exclusively for Members, this special figurine of Mackenzie expresses just how much we appreciate your loyalty as a Charming Tails Collector. Additionally, all Leaf & Acorn Club Members will also receive "This Is The Key," the official 2000 Charming Tails lapel pin.

EXCLUSIVE DESIGNS FOR MEMBERS ONLY

The first benefit of being a Leaf & Acorn Club Member is the opportunity to purchase "Peek-A-Boo Bouquet." This will be the first of the two figurines that will be available exclusively to Club Members in 2000. Members will receive a special order form for "Peek-A-Boo Bouquet" in their membership kit. This "Members Only" exclusive is priced at $22.00.

Later in the year an additional "Members Only" figurine and holiday ornament, created by Dean Griff, will become available. Introduction of these exclusive collectibles will be announced in the "Squashville Gazette" and by special mailing to all members. No member is under any obligation to purchase any "Members Only" product.

CHARMING TAILS CATALOG

A comprehensive 52-page, full-color catalog featuring all currently available figurines and ornaments will be included in your membership kit. A complete reference section documents all retired Charming Tails Collectibles.

"SQUASHVILLE GAZETTE"

Only Club Members will receive an annual subscription to the "Squashville Gazette." This newsletter will keep you up-to-date with the enchanting world of Charming Tails and on top of the behind-the-scenes scoop! Be one of the first to hear about new Charming Tails introductions and retirements.

INVITATIONS TO SPECIAL EVENTS

Members of the Leaf & Acorn Club will receive advance notice of and special invitations to attend in-store collector events, including personal appearances by Charming Tails artist Dean Griff.

MEMBERSHIP CARD

Your full-color membership card will be personalized with your name and membership number, identifying you as a loyal collector and Member of The Leaf & Acorn Club. Your membership card will serve as your passport to many unique and wonderful opportunities and surprises.

The Leaf & Acorn Club

2000 Leaf & Acorn Club Membership Application

Member Number

☐ **Please renew my Membership for $29.50.**
   (Please enter your Membership number in boxes at right.)

☐ **Please enroll me as a new Member for $29.50.**

The *Leaf & Acorn* Club ™

I am paying by ☐ **Check/Money Order** ☐ **Visa**
☐ **Discover** ☐ **Mastercard**

Credit Card #   Expiration Date

_____
Signature

Please provide one name per membership!

☐ Mr. ☐ Mrs. ☐ Ms.

First Name   MI   Last Name

Address 1

Address 2

City   State   Zip Code

Country   Day Phone   Evening Phone   Birthday

E-Mail Address

Join Today! Call 1 877 435 CLUB
THE LEAF & ACORN CLUB
PO BOX 972124
DALLAS, TX 75397-2124